למזל-טוב
# L'Mazeltov

## Your Personal Guide to
## Jewish Childbirth Education

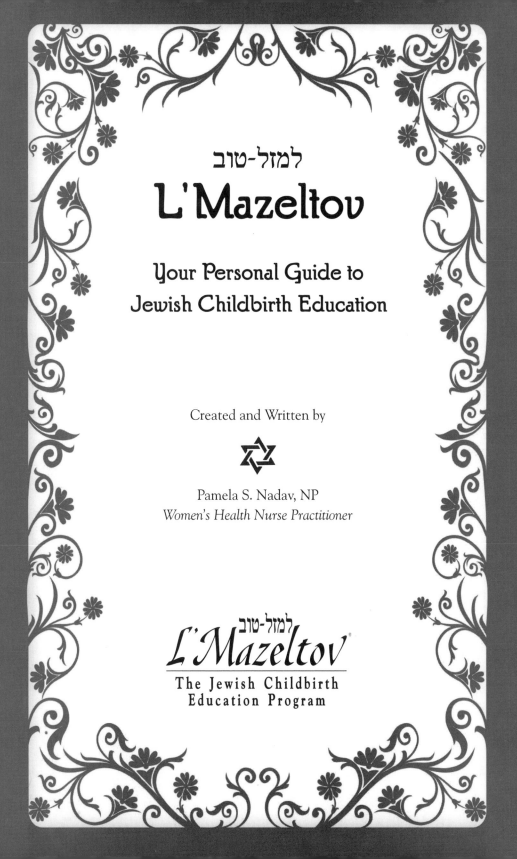

למזל-טוב

# L'Mazeltov

## Your Personal Guide to Jewish Childbirth Education

Created and Written by

Pamela S. Nadav, NP
*Women's Health Nurse Practitioner*

למזל-טוב
*L'Mazeltov*®
The Jewish Childbirth
Education Program

**L'Mazeltov®**
*The Jewish Childbirth Education Program*

L'Mazeltov, Inc.
P.O. Box 729
Carlsbad, CA 92018
Tel: 800 604-9844
www.lmazeltov.org

First Edition 2008

The L'Mazeltov Jewish Childbirth Education Program is for informational purposes only and is not meant as medical advice. Anyone using this product should consult with competent medical professionals before adopting any of these suggestions. The author and the publisher assume no responsibility for your actions.

For quantity orders or to become a L'Mazeltov Affiliate, please contact: baby@lmazeltov.org

Cover art by Karla Gudeon. *www.karlagudeon.com*

L'Mazeltov logo, cover, and book design by
CenterPointe Design. *www.CenterPointeDesign.com*

Printed in the United States of America

ISBN: 978-0-9778661-0-6

Library of Congress Control Number: 2008903697

"With Each
Child the World
Begins Anew."
—MIDRASH

*I dedicate this book to the*
*existence and strength of*
*our Jewish People*
*NOW and ALWAYS.*

# L'Mazeltov Disclaimer

Each woman is an individual with varying health histories. The information contained within L'Mazeltov needs to be verified by your own doctor or health care provider. Protocols may vary from doctor to doctor and state to state, so always follow your doctor's orders rather than L'Mazeltov or any other source. Not everything related to the subject of childbirth and Jewish life cycle education is included in L'Mazeltov and it does not replace a childbirth education course. L'Mazeltov strives to merely serve as a guide.

L'Mazeltov is just one of the many sources that you may review relating to pregnancy, childbirth and Jewish life cycle education. It is intended to be used as a reference source only. All pregnant women should seek the advice of a qualified medical professional. The information in this book should by no means be considered a substitute for the advice or judgment of your own personal physician.

Our main goal is to preserve and celebrate our traditions as a Jewish People. The emphasis is on our faith, culture, and importance of family. L'Mazeltov is not seeking to be "politically correct" or endorse a particular branch of Judaism. We strive to present an authentic display of information (to the best of our knowledge) and not a "watered-down version" of interpretation and opinion. It is not our intention to preach to anyone or hold ourselves out as experts in Judaism. We hope to convey a warm and loving experience in Judaism where all are welcomed and embraced.

All efforts have been made to ensure the accuracy of the information contained in this book as of the date published. The author and the publisher expressly disclaim responsibility for any adverse effects arising from the use of L'Mazeltov or the application of the information contained therein.

"Learning in old age is like writing on sand. Learning in youth is like engraving on stone."

—Solomon Ibn G'Verol

# Table of Contents

*"May you live to be a hundred and twenty."*

## Section I - Introduction

## Section II - Childbirth Education

CHAPTER ONE – THE BASICS

CHAPTER TWO – PRENATAL NUTRITION

# Section III ~ Jewish Life Cycle Education

# Section IV - Traditional L'Mazeltov Recipes

# Section V - Notes, Photos, Journaling & Conclusion

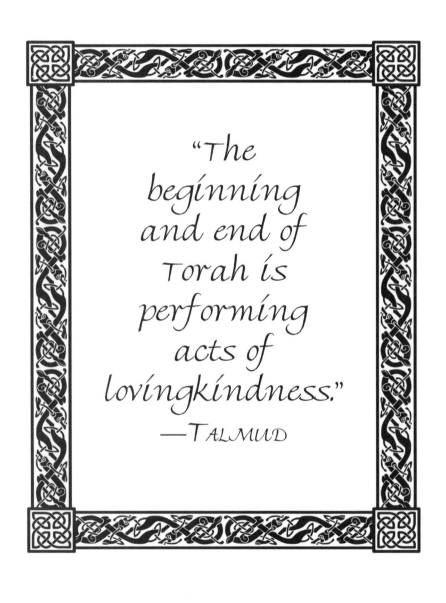

"The beginning and end of Torah is performing acts of lovingkindness."

—TALMUD

# SECTION I

# Introduction

"In the beginning . . . and G-d
saw that it was good."

—GENESIS

# Foreword

We live in an age of specialization. The store of knowledge in science, technology, medicine and most other fields of human endeavor has become so vast that no one mind can contain all of it. As a result, when you see your family doctor because of a medical problem, he or she may send you to a specialist who has concentrated in a given field of medicine, and may be more likely to know how to diagnose your condition, and how to treat it.

How surprising and refreshing, therefore, to come across an author who combines two specialties: her professional expertise in the field of women's health, in which she excels, and her passion for and knowledge of contemporary Jewish life, which she knows and practices with true joy.

If you care about women's health and you care about your baby—expected or recently born—then you will appreciate Pamela Nadav's ingenious idea of combining both of these issues and presenting them with the expertise and devotion each of them deserve. Both of them determine the life and well-being of mother and child; now and for generations to come.

Permit me to add that I have known Pamela practically all her life. I admire her achievements in her chosen fields of interest; but I value even more her loving, caring, kind and compassionate nature and her compelling need to help wherever she can.

This book is the product of a very good mind and a very good heart. Read it . . . you'll love it . . . and it will change your life "for good!"

—RABBI MARVIN BORNSTEIN,
LOS ANGELES, CA

# Welcome to L'Mazeltov

## "Each child Brings a Special Blessing into the World."

### "B'RUCHIM HABAIM"

After many years of teaching childbirth education classes, ongoing preparation, hours of soul searching, and endless prayers—L'Mazeltov, the book, is finally born. It is my pleasure to share L'Mazeltov with the expectant parents and families of the Jewish community. I hope that it will serve as a starting point , as you prepare for the sacred joy and responsibility of raising your Jewish baby.

Children watch how we live. Who we are shouts louder than anything we say or do as parents or teachers. What a wonderful closeness you can share together preparing spiritually, physically, and emotionally for your precious new baby!

## ABOUT L'MAZELTOV

L'Mazeltov™ is an integration of Childbirth with Jewish Life Cycle Education. It is a compilation of information collected over the years and is based on personal experiences, family stories, and years of research. L'Mazeltov is not meant to replace traditional childbirth education classes in any way. In fact, L'Mazeltov strongly recommends attending childbirth education classes, infant CPR, newborn care classes, lactation classes or any other pregnancy, childbirth education and child care and development courses. Reading about childbirth is a good start, but the experience can never be as beneficial as the one you will gain in a classroom setting. Currently, I am in the process of encouraging synagogues and Jewish centers to start L'Mazeltov programs at their facilities.

Volumes could be (and have been for centuries) written about Judaism in an attempt to provide an introduction to Jewish traditions, beliefs, prayers and practices. L'Mazeltov's main purpose is to provide traditional childbirth education and a basic introduction to Judaism.

L'Mazeltov embraces and respects all branches of Judaism and seeks to connect its readers to the beauty of Judaism and to unite rather than divide. As the creator of L'Mazeltov, I strongly recommend that you, the expectant Jewish couple, consider affiliating yourselves with the local synagogue or Jewish center of your choosing. I encourage you to make the process of exploring, learning and connecting an enjoyable priority. We want to be a part of your Jewish renewal and growth. Becoming part of a synagogue "Havurah"—Hebrew for circle of friends, is a wonderful way to connect and bond with other Jewish couples who have a similar commonality.

Together you can have a Shabbat blessing by the Rabbi. After you deliver your babies, your Havurah can return as a group for another Shabbat and form playgroups—the possibilities are endless! Community builds Immunity! Boost your immune system by forming healthy bonds of friendship. You will find it very beneficial to be connected with other families as your child is growing up.

L'Mazeltov offers Jewish expectant parents a glimpse into and a taste of Judaism for you and your new family.

B'shalom,

Pamela S. Nadav, NP

# WHY IS L'MAZELTOV DIFFERENT?

L'Mazeltov combines the vital essence of two Jewish expressions—"*L'chaim*" meaning "To Life" and "*Mazel Tov*," meaning "Good Fortune."

*Mazel* or *Mazal* literally means luck, but more specifically refers to good luck. The exclamation "*Mazel Tov!*", expressed at every joyous Jewish life-cycle event, is the same as saying, "Congratulations!" Judaism places the sanctity of life above all else, and the toast "*L'chaim*," meaning "To Life," conveys that defining belief. L'Mazeltov binds those two symbolic expressions together.

Why do we include Judaism in a book about childbirth education?

Because giving life is such an important concept in our Jewish tradition.

L'Mazeltov brings you the creative integration of traditional childbirth education and an introduction to Jewish life, traditions, values and philosophy, designed especially for expectant parents. With L'Mazeltov and a connection to a community of like-minded expectant parents, you can receive a high-quality introduction and education in a warm and supportive environment. L'Mazeltov offers you a variety of ways to create your own personalized Jewish parenting journey. Pregnancy is a time of tremendous change and preparation. L'Mazeltov is a resource for you to enhance your Jewish environment while learning vital information about your pregnancy and childbirth experience.

What a joy it is for families to create their own traditions! L'Mazeltov is a launching pad for creating your own customs, uniting generation to generation as you explore your options and plan your life together.

# PHILOSOPHY OF L'MAZELTOV

Jewish tradition speaks to us of the joy and the sacred privilege of parenthood that gives meaning and purpose to our existence. It emphasizes the specialness of each child, our most precious legacy, to the future of Judaism. Raising children is one of the fulfillments of a Jewish marriage. *"P'ru Huvvu"* is Hebrew for "Be Fruitful and Multiply."

It is with these thoughts in mind that I have created the concept of L'Mazeltov. For some of you, L'Mazeltov will be a "rebirth" of Jewish family life. For those who have chosen to embrace Judaism, it can be a golden opportunity to share in the beauty and traditions of Judaism as you prepare for your child's birth.

I would like to share with you the "spark" that has kindled the beginning seeds of L'Mazeltov. It has been said that if a child is raised with nothing, he will believe in everything.

While living on a kibbutz in Israel, I observed that many Jewish youth who were not raised with Jewish traditions or background were searching and yearning for spiritual roots. They were lost and had nothing  spiritual to follow. They traveled to various countries and embraced different religions or cults because they felt vacant in their souls. In the Diaspora, (Jews living outside Israel), the situation is even worse. This phenomenon really touched me deeply. When you give your children a traditional education and background, you give them something to identify with or rebel against, in order to forge their own identity.

Our Jewish people are becoming an Endangered Species! We need to preserve our precious Jewish traditions, and not let them all fade away. . . .

It is my hope and dream that the essence of L'Mazeltov will help plant strong roots of Judaism for your children in your homes.

# THANK YOU

L'Mazeltov has been my lifelong dream-come-true throughout most of my adult life. I want to give a big hug and Todah to my wonderful husband, Yoav, who is my angel. He starts my day each morning with a cup of coffee in bed. He supports my efforts and encourages my dreams. He is truly my *beshert*, my destiny, and he has a *neshama tovah*, a good soul.

My family has been very supportive and loving. I wish to thank each and every one of my children and grandchildren. I am truly blessed by their loyalty, love and support. L'Mazeltov has been in their lives for a very long time and they have been an inspiration to me. My family is my personal "Tree of Life" and I am very proud of them all.

My love for them is limitless and I pray daily that G-d will bless them with health and happiness, peace of mind, joy and love. May they all enjoy long, wonderful, meaningful and fulfilling lives.

# ACKNOWLEDGEMENTS

Rabbi Bornstein has been my personal Rabbi throughout my life. He has been a monumental part of my upbringing in preschool, sunday school, Hebrew school, Bat Mitzvah, confirmation, my wedding, many family events, and countless holidays. His kindness, spirit, and graciousness have been such a blessing in my life. I cherish Rabbi Bornstein and his wonderful wife, Miriam, for the Jewish spark they planted in my soul. They both honored my husband, Yoav, and myself at our wedding and made that day very special. I am very grateful and blessed for the privilege to have such a special Rabbi in my life.

Thank you to all who have contributed to my heartfelt endeavor by reading the text, offering feedback and suggestions, editing, and just being there for me when I needed to vent!

I am very grateful to Rabbi Baruch and Nechama Greenberg from the Chabad Center in Oceanside, California. The Greenbergs are so warm and gracious. They touch my soul and make me feel so welcomed and honored. Special thanks to Rabbi Lisa Goldstein, Executive Director, Hillel of San Diego for her time and effort in being a reader for my book. Thank you to Leta Gold who performs my "financial mikvah" so kindly. A special "Todah"—thank you to Dr. Moshe and Diana Zwang, authors of the book, *Palm Therapy*, whose insights and wisdom are unsurpassed. I appreciate and thank my dear friends, Alice Thomas and Ilene Bernstein, for taking the time to be such careful readers and give constructive comments to me. I appreciate the support and enthusiasm of Deborah Katz, Psychologist, Freddi Pakier, Sherry Brown, and Gwen Damsky-Cohen RN. Our dear friends, Nesta and Eitan Aharoni have been my breath of fresh air. I so appreciate the blossoming of ideas on our "walk and talks."

Thank you to Karla Gudeon, the talented artist whose painting graces the cover. She has been a pleasure to work with and I appreciate her beautiful work.

Thank you to my son Michael and his beautiful wife Tania, who have been so supportive and helpful with L'Mazeltov. Tania discovered Karla Gudeon's art on the web and she is a cherished "daughter" to me.

A big thank you to Matthew and Joan Greenblatt of CenterPointe Design in Vista, California, who made my dream become a reality.

I'd also like to acknowledge Dr. Einat DuHamel and Dr. Michelle Gerber, both Ob/Gyn's whose skills, wisdom and insights really added to the integrity of L'Mazeltov. Special thanks to Dr. Mark Moss for his encouraging words and actions of support for sharing L'Mazeltov with the Jewish community.

And last but not least, you—my readers—you are the cherished L'Mazeltov participants. Thank you for the gift of your presence, participation and acknowledgement.

# SECTION II

# Childbirth Education

"A baby enters the world with hands clenched, as if to say the world is mine and I shall grab it."

—MIDRASH

# CHAPTER ONE
# The Basics

*"With Each Child the World*
*Begins Anew."*
—Midrash

## CHILDBIRTH PREPARATION

Isn't it an awesome experience to be pregnant? Having a new life taking root inside your body is a miracle in itself. The childbirth education section of L'Mazeltov is designed to nurture the expectant mother, educate the family, and prepare for the most important event of your life—your baby's birthday! It is designed to simplify the overwhelming amount of information into bite-sized, easy to read portions. The overview of topics here will be a buffet of tools to use in order to maintain control and dignity throughout your preparation, labor, and the birth of your baby. Remember—it's most important to enjoy the journey!

Some of the topics include:
- The importance of prenatal fitness and prenatal nutrition.
- Common discomforts of pregnancy.
- What happens at your prenatal doctor visits?
- Sexual relations during pregnancy.
- Overview of breathing techniques, labor and relaxation techniques.

Childbirth Education

- Stages and phases of labor in detail.
- Methods of psychological anesthesia, including conditioning, concentration and discipline.
- Signs of labor.
- What to expect during labor and delivery.
- Back labor and hyperventilation.
- Toxemia of pregnancy.
- Types of anesthesia during labor and delivery, including epidurals.
- What are ultrasounds, fetal monitors, and amniocentesis?
- Cesarean section—the alternate mode of delivery.
- The Postpartum stage—birth to 6 weeks.
- Appearance of the newborn.
- Breastfeeding and bottlefeeding.

You can help yourself stay healthy and peaceful during your pregnancy by being well-rested; try to take a nap each day. Take a personal inventory of your lifestyle—becoming pregnant is the perfect time to renew yourself as you give life. Take time to reduce stress in your life by avoiding toxic, negative people and strained relationships. Eliminate tobacco and alcohol, and be your own best friend.

I remember flying on a commercial airline and watching the flight attendant describe the emergency procedures. The flight attendant said that in an emergency situation the oxygen masks would drop down and we were instructed to put the oxygen mask on ourselves before putting them on our children. This is not a natural motherly instinct, but it is important to follow these instructions in order to be able to assist our children. You need to nourish yourself first, so that you will be able to provide for your family and not become unhealthy.

Be prepared physically—moderate exercises such as walking 20 minutes per day is recommended. Be sure to check with your doctor or health-care provider before beginning any type of exercise. Practice all exercises and rehearse labor a few times each week. Be prepared emotionally and intellectually—ask questions, read, communicate with your doctor and become an active participant in your care. Seek out your family—make time to become closer and strengthen your support systems. Put yourself and your partner on the highest rung of the ladder; be close, hold hands, and enjoy this childbirth journey together. Arrange as much as you can in advance, such as:

- Protect your mattress with a waterproof mattress pad.
- Check supplies for the baby and arrange for newborn care.
- Pack your suitcase and labor bag.
- Be in touch with your labor coach (cell phones are best for this).
- Arrange for an alternate person to help during labor in case of illness.
- Prepare for help at home when you return from the hospital.
- Take a tour and register at the hospital.
- Be familiar with alternate routes to the hospital in case of a detour.
- Plan for care of other children, pets, and plants.

## FORMING YOUR PARTNERSHIP

*"Say little and do much."*
—THE TALMUD

The relationship between you and your husband is very important. Take the time to share your feelings and expectations about the childbirth experience in order to promote bonds of trust and intimacy between the two of you. Assess your own personal emotional climate when you share facts and feelings. Together, your anxiety is lessened when you communicate well. The goal is to be a present, active participant, not a passive bystander. Take ownership and responsibility of your pregnancy path. Reinforce a positive attitude towards pregnancy and childbirth. During labor, you will feel less tension and experience security and comfort when you are surrounded by a caring, sympathetic circle of family and friends. You will also recover more quickly both physically and emotionally if you have created a solid support system.

# CHOOSING YOUR LABOR BUDDY/COACH

*"Better a neighbor who is near*
*than a brother who is far."*
—PROVERBS

Choose your labor buddy (your labor coach) early in your pregnancy. Labor buddies can be husbands, family members or friends, or a combination thereof. You can have more than one labor buddy or a back-up labor buddy just in case. Labor buddy = teamwork = support. Coaching is a labor of love and provides vital support to the woman during pregnancy and during her labor. A good labor buddy provides comfort and support and has patience to cope with your fluctuating moods while open to discussing your fears about birth and parenthood. A labor buddy will also support you through the nausea and fatigue as well as your concerns about your changing body image. It is highly beneficial to build your support team early in your pregnancy. Together you can prepare for the "oys and joys" of pregnancy, labor, and delivery. Your labor buddy will be participating in your plans to attend childbirth education classes, lactation classes, and baby-care classes, and will be with you throughout your labor and the delivery of your new baby.

*L'Mazeltov*

# A NOTE TO PARENTS ABOUT SELF CARE

*"You should live to be a hundred and twenty."*
—JEWISH SAYING

As parents, our children need us to be as healthy and balanced as we can be. Our children glean strength from our strength, and feel safe when we are grounded and balanced. If we run ourselves ragged in an attempt to care for everyone else, if we work so long and hard that we have no time or energy to participate in family activities or if we sacrifice our marital relationship for "the sake of the children," we are actually doing our children a disservice. By ensuring that we as individuals and our relationship are healthy, balanced, nourished, trustworthy and stable, we will be providing a vital foundation, emotionally and physically, for our children. What children want most is our presence and our participation.

# MENTAL HEALTH RECOMMENDATIONS

*"All beginnings are difficult."*
—MIDRASH

Do you know that pregnancy causes major hormonal fluctuations? Your body is experiencing many changes physically and hormonally, and these changes have an impact on your emotional and mental well-being. It is even more important during this time to be conscious and take steps to keep your body and mind in balance. Keeping hydrated, drinking six to eight glasses of water per day, and eating small meals every two to three hours is very advisable. You want to "graze" all day long, avoiding getting too hungry or too full. Eating a balanced diet and keeping physically fit can help you to keep emotionally stable during pregnancy. Moderate daily exercise is advised, under the care of your physician, but keep in mind that your goals are different when you are pregnant. Prior to being pregnant, you were able to do more strenuous exercises. During pregnancy, you want to avoid fatigue, shortness of breath, and sweating. Regarding exercise, the motto "no pain, no gain" does not apply to pregnant women.

At your first OB visit, you will have a complete medical exam and lab work that may include a blood test for TSH—Thyroid Simulating Hormone. However, the TSH test is not a routine or mandatory part of the prenatal panel. Hypothyroid (a low thyroid) or hyperthyroid (over-active thyroid) conditions can manifest due to the hormonal changes of pregnancy and may have a hereditary component, as well. Symptoms related to mental health may include depression, anxiety and feelings of panic. Sometimes previous anxiety, panic, or depression symptoms can worsen during pregnancy and sometimes these symptoms may actually improve during pregnancy. These symptoms may or may not be associated with an abnormal thyroid condition. Regardless, it is my personal advice to be aware of your TSH levels throughout your life and especially during pregnancy.

At your OB visits, it is vital to communicate any psychological symptoms in addition to your physical symptoms. There are medications that are safe in pregnancy to treat depression, panic attacks, and anxiety. Contact your doctor and he or she will prescribe what is safe for you and your baby in utero. Knowing your family history will allow you to be more aware of possible conditions that can occur during this time. Some conditions may be genetically, hormonally or environmentally linked. Most of you have heard of Postpartum Depression or "Baby Blues", which happens after the baby is born. It is important to be aware of possible emotional changes while you are pregnant, as well. Your doctor, health-care team, family and friends are all part of your support system that will help you through any crisis. Keep your scheduled OB appointments throughout your pregnancy and be sure to report any changes in your physical and emotional well-being in-between your appointments so that all your physical and mental health needs can be addressed.

L'Mazeltov

# CHAPTER TWO
# Prenatal Nutrition

*"Everyone is kneaded out of the same dough,
but not baked in the same oven."*
—YIDDISH PROVERB

## NUTRITION DURING PREGNANCY

Speaking about food and nutrition, this may be a good time to start reciting the *Hamotzi* prayer before meals (see page 181 of the Jewish Life Cycle section). With all of its challenges and discoveries, pregnancy is a wonderful opportunity to add to your repertoire of Jewish experience.

We talk about holiday foods at special occasions, but daily meals shared together are so important to our well-being and peace in the home. One of my best memories of sitting together at the dining room table and sharing a meal comes from my childhood. This meal is known in my family as the "Tanta Seba" lunch. My Tanta Seba was my great aunt and she was known for bringing the family together at her dining room table. The "Tanta Seba" lunch consisted of tuna mixed with hard boiled eggs in mayonnaise, rye bread, pumpernickel, mixed salad with Russian dressing (1000 island), green and yellow summer squash, kugel, and wedges of cantaloupe and honey dew melon. For dessert, we enjoyed mandlebrot and Swee Touch Nee tea! (See recipes for the kugel and mandelbrot in our recipe section). We sat for hours at Tanta Seba's dining room table enjoying this delicious lunch and warm atmosphere.

When my Tanta Seba passed away, she left me a small money gift that I used to buy a dining room table and chairs set in order to carry on her tradition of family time at the table. My husband and I are now the hub of the family, and we enjoy many family meals in our home.

Parenting actually begins before conception and continues during your pregnancy. As a new parent, one of the most important tasks will be caring for and providing for your new baby. Your first act of parenting is to maintain a healthy diet for yourself and your baby. This has far-reaching implications and begins even before you conceive. For example, your levels of folate or folic acid, a B vitamin, are important at the time of conception and thus need to be at adequate levels prior to conception. By acting on your commitment to provide the best care possible for your child, you will be protecting yourself and supporting your baby's development at the same time. Your developing baby is dependent on you to provide all the nutrients he or she will receive. It is recommended to include plenty of fluids. The amount of water recommended per day is 6 to 8 glasses. But avoid too much water intake because it can dilute your electrolyte balance, which can result in serious complications.

Often, the hormones related to pregnancy will bring about changes in cravings, dietary preferences, eating habits and tolerance for foods. Foods that you love you may now hate and foods that you once hated you may now crave. During my first pregnancy, I had a strong craving for chopped liver on rye with a pickle and a cream soda. I could eat this day and night! I was a regular customer at the deli counter at the market. Some cravings of inedible substances, such as dirt, may reflect a deficiency in your diet and need to be reported right away to your doctor. Some women experience an increase in appetite, while others find that their appetite has decreased. Some women may experience "morning sickness", which is nausea and mostly occurs in the first trimester of pregnancy. Communication with your physician will help you ensure that your dietary needs are addressed.

During pregnancy, it is wise to discontinue drinking all alcoholic beverages. Alcohol has been linked to birth defects, mental retardation, and stunted physical growth. Cigarette smoking during pregnancy can impact a baby's development and put you at risk for pre-term labor, and therefore should be avoided. Always check with your doctor before taking any medication. Even over-the-counter drugs and herbal supplements can pass through the placenta to your baby and certain drugs can cause birth defects.

Pregnancy itself can be a stressful period, with numerous changes happening in your body, your emotional world and in your life. Reducing stress wherever you can will support you as an individual and as a couple. Making mealtimes as happy, healthy, easy and stress-free as possible can have a positive impact on your overall emotional and physical health and well-being. Working together as a couple, planning ahead, keeping it simple and allowing time for meals will lessen your stress and make life a bit more manageable. Knowing you have healthy foods on hand, when you need or want a snack, will make it more likely that you will use your calories as wisely as possible. Throughout your pregnancy, eating a healthy snack every 2-3 hours and eating several small meals throughout your day will help maintain your blood sugar at a more constant level, an important key to your health and stamina during pregnancy.

*Here are some healthy snack suggestions:*

PROTEIN

Mixed nuts, hard boiled eggs, bean dip, chicken breast slices.

DAIRY

Cheese and crackers, cottage cheese and fruit, yogurt, pudding.

FRUITS AND VEGETABLES

Variety of fresh fruits, fresh veggie platter, vegetable soup (low salt), fruit smoothie.

GRAINS

Granola bars, whole grain crackers, bran muffins, variety of pastas.

There are many books on the subject of nutrition during pregnancy. In this section, L'Mazeltov wishes to provide you with a sampling of basic nutritional suggestions. What you eat while pregnant will provide the building blocks for your baby's healthy development, so be sure to check with your health-care provider to determine your optimal personal nutritional intake for your baby and yourself while you are pregnant. Did you know that the Bible mentions pomegranates, nuts and raisins as foods that promote fertility?

First, it's important to understand that the concept of eating for two does not translate to double the calories. Your intake of calories generally only increases by approximately 300 calories per day while you are pregnant, and a well-rounded diet includes a variety of foods and should be high in fiber.

The March of Dimes suggests including 2-4 servings per day of fruit, 3-5 servings per day of vegetables, 6-11 servings per day of grains, 3-4 servings per day of protein and 3-4 servings per day of milk products (calcium rich foods). Keep in mind that while you are pregnant you should avoid certain fish, such as shark, swordfish, king mackerel, raw fish (shellfish) or white snapper, because they contain high levels of mercury. Avoid soft cheeses, such as feta, brie, camembert, blue-veined, and Mexican-style cheese, because they may be unpasteurized and could cause Listeria infection.

Some doctors suggest that all meals should include protein, calcium and folate since these nutrients are so essential to the wellbeing of your baby. To ensure you are meeting all your nutritional vitamin and mineral requirements, your doctor may recommend that you take a prenatal vitamin supplement. It may be a prescription prenatal vitamin or an over the counter brand.

Protein is essential to your baby's cell growth and blood production. Generally, a pregnant woman requires 80-100 grams of protein daily. Good protein sources can include lean meats, poultry, eggs, beans, fish, peanut butter, tofu and nuts. Eating a variety of foods will help ensure that the essential protein needs for you and your baby are met.

The National Institute of Health states that folate protects against neural tube defects, including malformations of the spine, skull and brain. The recommended daily allowance (RDA) for pregnant women is 400-600 micrograms of folic acid per day from food sources and/or dietary supplements. Folate can be found in dark green leafy vegetables, dark yellow fruits and veggies, lima beans, black beans, black-eyed peas, chickpeas and fortified grains.

Calcium plays a vital role in building and maintaining healthy bones for you and your growing baby. In addition, this mineral helps to conduct nerve impulses and aids in the proper function of your baby's heart and other muscles. The recommended daily allowance (RDA) of calcium during pregnancy is 1200 milligrams per day, which is equivalent to approximately four cups of milk daily. Some other yummy sources of calcium include yogurt, cheeses, cottage cheese and non-dairy products such as collards, spinach, broccoli, okra, chickpeas (garbanzo beans), lentils, sweet potatoes and tofu. In addition, foods such as orange juice, cereal, breads and cereal bars are often fortified with calcium.

This is just a sampling of what you will need nutritionally in order to provide for yourself and your baby while you are pregnant. It serves as a guide to a well designed, balanced and complete nutritional plan specifically geared towards your pregnancy. The good news is that for today's expectant moms, quality health and nutrition information is readily available to help you ensure that your precious growing baby can have the best start in life!

## CHAPTER THREE
# Prenatal Muscle Toning Exercises

*"Exercise your faith,
walk with G-d."*
—SOLOMON IBN G'VIROL

## BODY MECHANICS

Proper body mechanics will help protect your body and help you feel better throughout your pregnancy. Check with your doctor regarding the specifics of proper body mechanics and prenatal exercises. The following are some general recommendations.

### Posture

Good posture protects you from backache. Avoid standing in one place for too long. Change your position every hour or two and avoid long car trips. Good posture prevents fatigue and helps you look and feel much better. Maintaining good posture helps to promote good circulation.

### Sitting

Sit cross-legged on the floor. This position helps to strengthen your pelvic floor muscles and stretch your thigh muscles. Shake out your legs frequently and rotate your ankles to improve circulation. When you sit on a chair, avoid crossing your legs. Use every opportunity to elevate your legs and arms, such as in a recliner (this is a great gift idea for the expectant mother).

### Bending

Avoid bending from the waist, especially when lifting something. Avoid lifting heavy objects. Use your legs to spare your back. It's advisable to squat with your back straight and, better yet, ask someone else to bend down and pick it up for you.

### Lying Down and Getting Up

When getting ready to lie down or get up, first lie on your side and then roll onto your back to avoid straining your abdominal muscles. To get in a side-lying position, which is the best position for sleep, place one pillow under your head and use additional pillows as desired for your comfort, such as one pillow between your knees. It helps to support your top leg, arm and uterus with one or more pillows. Towards the end of your pregnancy, avoid resting flat on your back; instead use a blanket or pillow wedge to tilt yourself to one side. To avoid compression of your major vessels, it is recommended to lie on either side, but the left side is best for circulation.

# A WORD ABOUT EXERCISE

Get your doctor's permission before doing any kind of exercise. Do not exercise if you experience any pain, bleeding or fatigue. Exercise on a stable surface. Take a nice deep breath before and after each exercise. Use caution to exercise slowly and discontinue exercise if any discomfort occurs. Proceed cautiously and gently when beginning any exercise program. Specific prenatal exercises can promote circulation to the growing uterus. It can help relieve lower-back discomfort, and can strengthen and support the growing uterus prior to delivery. Prenatal exercise decreases varicose veins in the legs and also decreases the chance of developing hemorrhoids, which are varicose veins in the rectum. A 20-40% increase in blood volume circulating in your body while you are pregnant makes doctor-supervised prenatal exercise even more important for enhancing circulation and promoting overall health. Note: It is recommended that you keep your heart rate under 140 bpm (beats per minute).

# EXERCISES TO BE DONE DAILY

A really nice way to exercise together as a couple is to go on a 20 minute walk every day. This is an excellent form of exercise and promotes good circulation, a healthy appetite, and a feeling of well-being. My favorite "soulwalk" is at the beach early in the morning or later in the evening! It is so refreshing for my body and soul. Make sure that you are exercising when it's cool outside—early in the day or in the evening—not in the hot sun, and only with your doctor's approval.

**Pelvic Floor Exercises.** (Kegel Exercises . . . "not Kugel!")
  *Kegel exercises are the tightening and relaxing of the pelvic floor muscles.*
Do your Kegel exercises 100 times per day for the rest of your life. You can split this up into 20 repetitions 5 times a day. Think of your pelvic floor like an elevator. Imagine going up in an elevator while drawing up the pelvic floor muscles. When you reach your limit, descend floor by floor again, release even more and then go to the "basement." The same muscles can also be exercised when urinating by stopping and starting the flow of urine several times. During intercourse, these muscles can tighten and relax to enhance your sexual experience.

**Helpful Hints:**
You can do Kegels anytime, anywhere! No one can see you doing them unless you make funny faces. Do your Kegels while waiting for a red light to turn green, talking on the telephone, or waiting for a TV

commercial to end. Add more exercises to your daily regimen that include the pelvic rock and pelvic tilt.

## Pelvic Rock.

*Do this exercise several times a day, five repetitions each time.*
Kneel on all fours, making a box with your body. Put your knees underneath your hips, hands underneath the shoulders, head straight, back straight. Pull in your abdominal muscles and buttocks and press up with your lower back. And then relax, but do not let your back sag. You can do the pelvic rock while you're standing as well. With the knees slightly bent and arms held with palms forward, pull up your pelvis in front with the abdominal muscles and then down at the back with your buttock muscles.

## Tension Relievers.

*To be done several times per day, four repetitions each time.*
Sit cross-legged (which is known as Tailor sitting) on the floor and slowly roll your head in a circle and then change direction and repeat. Sit in a Tailor sitting position, raise your shoulders to your ears, and raise them up and down.

## CHAPTER FOUR

# Common Discomforts during Pregnancy

*"Use good posture and eat five to six small meals a day."*

## THE FOURTEEN DISCOMFORTS

The following list includes common discomforts of pregnancy. These discomforts occur generally at any time during pregnancy, but tend to develop towards the last trimester of pregnancy. This information will allow you to better understand the physiological changes of pregnancy and the impact these changes can have on your body. This knowledge can help to lessen your anxiety should these problems occur. Shortness of breath accompanied by chest pain, however, should be reported to your doctor immediately.

### 1. *Shortness of breath*

This is very common due to the pressure of the fundus (top of the uterus) on the diaphragm breathing muscle. It helps to have the head of your bed elevated 30 degrees. You can use two or three pillows to do this. Choose a bra that is not too tight. When the baby "drops"—that is, the presenting part is engaged in the birth canal—there will be some relief from this respiratory problem.

*L'Mazeltov*

## 2. *Varicose veins and hemorrhoids*

This problem is due to the increased blood volume during pregnancy, poor muscle tone, hereditary pre-disposition, and constricting clothing. Your doctor may recommend the use of pregnancy support hose in order to enhance the circulation in your legs. Exercise and warm baths may also help. Over the counter hemorrhoid preparations and hemorrhoid wipes are safe to use during pregnancy.

## 3. *Heartburn*

This is when the stomach acids regurgitate into the esophagus. Progesterone is a hormone produced by the placenta which causes a generalized relaxation of the digestive processes which can lead to a temporary acid-reflux condition. The growing uterus also displaces the stomach. Only take medications approved by your doctor. Be aware that bicarbonate of soda may cause fluid retention because of the high sodium content. There are some over-the-counter remedies that your doctor may recommend. Use good posture and eat five to six small meals a day in order to lessen these symptoms.

## 4. *Constipation*

This is caused by the same reasons as heartburn and also due to the iron supplements that your doctor often prescribes. It is important to exercise to increase abdominal muscle tone, and to promote circulation. Drinking six to eight glasses of water per day and adding dietary fiber, such as fruits, vegetables and grains, can also help. Keep in mind that prolonged constipation may cause hemorrhoids and your doctor may prescribe over-the-counter stool softeners to help alleviate your discomfort.

## 5. *Stretch marks*

Sometimes described as "ripples in a tree trunk that have borne fruit." Stretch marks are reddish, slightly indented streaks on the skin that appear primarily on the abdomen but also on the breasts and thighs. I thought that I avoided stretch marks with my first pregnancy when I reached my due date and still had a smooth belly. I was very surprised when I was 2 days past my due date and I had sprouted stretch marks overnight! Stretch marks occur when the skin is stretched due to rapid growth during pregnancy. Little can be done to prevent stretch marks and some people have a hereditary predisposition to develop them. Rubbing the skin with emollients such as cocoa butter and aloe cream helps prevent the itching of overstretched skin, but has no effect on their formation. I am not aware of any product currently on the market that will actually prevent them. The angry reddish appearance of stretch marks will become more subtle and silvery in color over time.

### 6. Urinary frequency

This is due to the pressure of the growing uterus on the bladder as well as an increase in urine production. It is wise to locate in advance the proximity of the nearest bathroom when setting out from your home! You should be aware that you may be more prone to urinary tract infections. Some preventive measures that can reduce your risk of bladder infections include drinking six to eight glasses of water daily and one eight ounce glass of cranberry juice daily. However, if you should have any symptoms of frequency, urgency or pain related to urination, report these symptoms to your doctor immediately. In addition, if you have a fever and notice pain in the lower to middle back area, you may have something even more serious, such as a kidney infection and you should call your doctor right away.

### 7. Low backache

This is due to the postural adjustments that result from your changing center of gravity. Doing the pelvic-rock and pelvic-tilt exercises can offer relief. It can also be helpful to do a simple "cat stretch" exercise by resting on all fours, your hands and knees on mat or floor with your hands shoulder width apart. Then flex your spine by arching your back up toward the ceiling. Wearing low-heeled shoes and including rest periods during the day can also provide relief from low backache.

### 8. Leg cramps

This is a very common complaint. Leg cramps occur due to increased blood volume and changes in your circulation. Leg cramps can also be caused by too much or inadequate calcium. The intense pain in your calf during a leg cramp can be relieved by stretching your leg and flexing your ankles while forcing your toes upward. In other words, pointing your toes can contribute to leg cramping.

## 9. *Pigmentation changes*

The hormones Estrogen and Progesterone are produced in higher concentration during pregnancy. The increased levels of these hormones cause pigmentation changes in the skin. The areola (dark area around the nipple) becomes larger and darker. Cholasma, known as "the mask of pregnancy," are brownish patches that appear on the face. Linea Nigra is a vertical streak on the abdomen from the pubis to the umbilicus. Some traces of these pigmentation changes may remain after pregnancy. Vascular changes in the skin include Palmar Erythema, resulting in reddish spots or marks on the palms of the hands and soles of the feet caused by increased blood flow to the capillaries, which are also known as "vascular spiders."

## 10. *Bleeding gums*

This is due to increased blood volume and higher levels of estrogen during pregnancy. The gums become softer during this time and dental work may be more uncomfortable. It is advisable to have regular dental visits before and during your pregnancy to ensure good dental health and to prevent gum disease, which can cause added risks during pregnancy.

## 11. *Vaginal discharge*

Vaginal discharge increases and becomes thickened and whitish during pregnancy. Yeast and bacterial infections are more prevalent during pregnancy. If you experience vaginal itching, irritation, redness or odor, consult your doctor for treatment.

## 12. *Enlarged and tender breasts*

Due to the hormones of pregnancy, your breasts may be tender and become enlarged during the first trimester. The ductal systems are being formed in the breasts after the fifth or sixth month of pregnancy. Colostrum, which is the "first milk," may or may not be present. A properly fitting bra should be worn for support due to the heaviness and increased size of the breasts.

### 13. *Feeling hot all the time*
Did someone turn on the heater? When you are pregnant, you feel a lot warmer due to hormones of pregnancy. My last month of pregnancy was August in Los Angeles, and I was miserable with no air conditioning. Most every day, I went to the air conditioned movie theater (with my chopped liver sandwich) to sit in the coldness for a few hours. I didn't care what the movie was about and I usually took a nap, too.

### 14. *Other possible discomforts of pregnancy may occur.*
Discuss any concerns with your doctor.

# CHAPTER FIVE

# Myths of Childbirth

*"Approach this experience with as much
knowledge and confidence
as possible."*

## FIVE MYTHS

**MYTH #1**: *"If only I did more . . ."*

Many pregnant women feel that if they read every book, exercise daily, and practice breathing and relaxation techniques religiously, this will guarantee them a perfect labor and delivery and baby. If this does not turn out to be perfect in all categories, they feel like less of a woman or a failure or that their husband is a failure, as well. This puts tremendous strain on you and your relationship as a couple. Don't beat yourself up; do the best you can to enjoy this life-changing journey. Some common misconceptions are that other women are stronger and can do better than you can. There are no 100% guarantees in life; be grateful for the opportunity to learn and experience pregnancy and childbirth, and accept the "ups and downs", just like any other part of your life.

**MYTH #2**: *"I'll be skinny after I give birth . . ."*

I was 21 years old when I gave birth to my first child, and I really believed that after I gave birth I would immediately fit into my slim jeans and button-down top. I couldn't wait to put on my regular clothes. What a shock! I needed to buy a "muu-muu" (big Hawaiian dress) in the hospital gift shop to wear home. Do yourself a favor and pack loose sweats with a drawstring and a loose-fitting t-shirt. After you give birth, your body needs to go through the period of involution when the uterus contracts down to a smaller size. It's normal to look like you are about five months pregnant when you leave the hospital. Your breasts will also be larger, since they will be filled with milk, and it's likely that the buttons on your shirt won't even reach across! Loose t-shirts are the best choice during this time.

**MYTH #3:** *"I don't need any childbirth classes because I'm having an epidural . . ."*

Some expectant parents feel that they don't need to take any classes to prepare for childbirth because they will just have an epidural! Even if you are planning to have an epidural, you may have to go through hours of labor before you can qualify to have an epidural (see anesthesia section). This is because you need to be at least three to four centimeters dilated, with regular, strong contractions, and often an epidural can slow down the intensity and regularity of your uterine contractions. You may also need a hormone called Pitocin to augment your labor if your labor contractions are not strong enough or close enough together. It is vitally important to be prepared for all aspects of pregnancy and childbirth, even if you choose to have an epidural. Do yourself a favor; approach this experience with as much knowledge and confidence as possible so that you will have a more positive birth experience! Keep in mind that it is better to learn what you may not need, rather than need what you have not learned.

**MYTH #4:** *"I want my make-up and my hair perfect and I don't want my body exposed while I'm in labor . . ."*

The word modesty does not exist while you're in labor. During labor you will sweat and swear, and your best friends will be a cold wet washcloth and a fan. The words you will long to hear will be "contraction is over."

The loss of modesty during labor is a given. You will feel very vulnerable and exposed but you will not care once your labor progresses. You will just want the baby out and in your loving arms.

**MYTH #5:** *"I will instantly feel like a mother . . ."*

After giving birth, most women feel exhausted, hungry and want to be cleaned up and fed before they can truly enjoy and nurture their new baby. Don't feel guilty about this! You may recall in Psychology 101 you learned about *Maslow's Hierarchy of Human Needs*. According to Maslow, you need your physical needs taken care of first—food, shelter, and physical comforts before you can go out and enjoy the theater or an art show. You need to take care of yourself first, before you can take care of another human being, even if that human being is your own new baby! After you wash, eat a meal and get some sleep, you will then begin the bonding journey with your precious newborn. Time and shared experience will help the bonding process to blossom and grow. Be patient and easy on yourself—your maternal feelings will gradually increase day by day.

# CHAPTER SIX
# Sex during Pregnancy

*"This is not a
'one-size fits all' subject."*

## IS IT OKAY TO HAVE
## SEX DURING PREGNANCY?

*It is essential to check with your doctor regarding sexual relations during pregnancy and any other questions or concerns you may have. This is not a "one-size fits all" subject. There are individual variations and you need to confer with your doctor on your specific situation. The following are some commonly-asked questions regarding sex during pregnancy:*

1. **Can having sexual intercourse cause a miscarriage?**
Generally, sexual intercourse does not cause a woman to miscarry. Women with a prior history of miscarriage are sometimes advised to avoid intercourse during the first three months of pregnancy. Women who have pre-term labor (cramping) and/or vaginal bleeding should not have intercourse at all. The concern is not only penetration during sexual intercourse but also the uterine contractions from orgasm (by any method).

## 2. Can having sexual intercourse hurt the baby?

Not likely, since the baby is well protected in the mother's uterus and the penis will not come in contact with the baby. Different positions may be tried as the baby grows and the size of the woman's belly increases with the length of the pregnancy. Missionary position can be uncomfortable due to the weight on your growing uterus. A good suggestion is a side-lying or a "spooning" position or female on top.

## 3. Is it normal for the genitals to look larger while pregnant?

Yes, both the genitalia and breasts become enlarged during pregnancy due to hormones and the increased blood flow to these areas.

## 4. Can a pregnant woman induce labor with sexual relations?

During the last trimester, nipple stimulation can trigger the release of your own natural Oxytocin, which can cause uterine contractions. Orgasm by any method can also cause uterine contractions when the cervix is "ripe." There is some speculation that the Prostaglandin hormone is present in the semen and may be a potential trigger to start labor. So, technically, sexual relations could lead to labor, but usually the uterine contractions subside in a few minutes and don't lead to true labor.

## 5. How soon before the delivery date should you stop having intercourse?

In most cases, a couple can continue gentle sexual intercourse and sexual expression as long as it is mutually comfortable. The obvious exceptions would be in the case of pre-term labor, any vaginal bleeding, Placenta Previa, or the rupture of the membranes. If the cervix has begun to dilate, intercourse should be avoided.

## 6. How soon after the delivery can intercourse be resumed?

This depends on how you feel and if you had a complicated vaginal delivery or a cesarean section. Generally, it is best to wait for your six-week postpartum checkup to make sure that you have healed properly, that your cervix has closed and also to discuss birth control. It's important to wait until the lochia (bleeding which follows delivery) has completely subsided for at least one full week prior to resuming intercourse.

### 7. *Will it hurt me to resume sexual intercourse?*

Due to the changes in your hormones, vaginal lubrication may be less than before you got pregnant. It is advisable to use a water-soluble lubricant like K-Y products, available in markets and drug stores. Avoid petroleum-based products as they may increase the discomfort. Take time to relax. You may need to do more touching. In the beginning, intercourse may be uncomfortable, so it is advisable to be patient. Keep in mind that you may need to use lubricants during intercourse while you are lactating. Your estrogen levels are lower while you are breastfeeding, which contributes to vaginal dryness.

### 8. *Will you feel different to your husband after having a baby?*

You may feel differently both physically and emotionally after giving birth. Physically there will be some adjustment time depending on the type of delivery you had. Vaginally you may feel the same, tighter, or looser than you did prior to childbirth. Sometimes the vaginal muscles lose some elasticity. You can try doing Kegel exercises (see page 16 for explanation of Kegel exercises) as they may improve and help you regain muscle tone. If discomfort persists for you and your husband, make sure you consult your doctor.

# SEXUAL RELATIONS IN PREGNANCY IN THE LAST TRIMESTER

Sexual response and activity may change during pregnancy and may vary widely from couple to couple. Knowing this can be reassuring. In most circumstances, sexual activity is not injurious to the baby. Physical expressions of love, including intercourse, are extremely important during pregnancy and help maintain intimacy and emotional equilibrium. There are no hard and fast rules about sexual activity in the last trimester. The following are circumstances where you should check with your doctor prior to engaging in sexual relations: you have a "deeply engaged presenting part" (i.e., the baby's head is "very low" in the pelvis), ruptured membranes (i.e., when the "bag of waters" breaks), any vaginal bleeding, or if the cervix has begun to dilate. Otherwise, studies show that lovemaking through the final weeks of pregnancy can be continued as long as it is comfortable and both partners want to. The baby is generally well protected in the mother's uterus, floating in a sac of amniotic fluid above the cervix, and blocked from the vagina by a mucous plug. There are some studies that indicate that sexual stimulation can speed up labor. Stimulation of the breasts and other erogenous zones in early stages of labor releases the hormone Oxytocin that makes labor and delivery progress more rapidly. Expectant parents should have active and honest communication with their doctor about sexual relations and all aspects of their progressing pregnancy. If relations must discontinue for some medical consideration, both the husband as well as the wife should be informed. Both expectant parents need to be reassured that they are loved and desirable in spite of the changes in body image that come with pregnancy.

# CHAPTER SEVEN

# Initial Doctor's Visit

*"It is such a blessing
to be pregnant."*

## WHAT HAPPENS FIRST

Usually when you are between eight and ten weeks pregnant, you will have your first OB appointment. This will be your longest appointment. Your weight, blood pressure, and other vital signs will be checked. Your doctor will help you to determine your "Estimated Date of Confinement" (i.e., your due date or EDC). Your due date is generally derived from your Last Menstrual Period (LMP). The doctor will be checking your urine for the presence of glucose and protein. Your fundal height will be checked after 20 weeks. This is measured in centimeters with a tape measure from the pubic hairline to the top of the fundus, which is the top of the uterus. You will have a complete physical, a pelvic exam, a Pap smear, and cultures for Chlamydia and Gonorrhea. OB labs generally include your blood type and RH, a CBC with a differential, possibly a TSH (Thyroid Stimulating Hormone) blood test, urine for culture and sensitivity, and tests for Syphilis, Rubella, Hepatitis B and HIV. A test for Cystic Fibrosis is also generally offered. For those of Jewish descent, a Tay Sachs test is recommended. You may also be given a limited pelvic sonogram to evaluate how many babies are in the uterus, the size of your baby which is the measurement from the crown rump length (i.e., the top of the baby's head to its tushie), and to check visually for cardiac action (basically viewing the movement of the baby's heart). The limited pelvic ultrasound will assess the amniotic fluid volume and check the status of your ovaries.

Generally, you will be checked every month until 28 weeks, then every two weeks thereafter until the 36th week, and then weekly from 36 weeks on. Different assessments and tests are done at various appointments. Many of these tests are time-sensitive, so it is important to keep every one of your appointments. Keep in mind that these are general guidelines and that each doctor will have his or her recommendations for appointments.

The term "AMA" means Advanced Maternal Age; generally this applies to a pregnant woman who will be age 35 years old or greater when she delivers her baby. If your status is AMA, you will likely have a few extra tests offered at your first appointment. Since there are potentially more risks involved when you are AMA, your formal ultrasound may be done earlier, and you may also be offered genetic counseling.

It is a good idea to bring a list of questions to your OB appointment. Your first OB appointment is very informative. At this appointment, you will also find out the name of the hospital where you will deliver, and information on hospital tours, childbirth education, infant CPR, and lactation classes. Also, if you have other children, sibling preparation classes are advisable.

Make sure you keep all your doctor appointments. You are the most important player on your team to help ensure you have a safe pregnancy and a healthy baby. This is your opportunity to interact with your doctor and get your questions answered, so be sure to write down any questions or concerns you might have and bring your list to your doctor's office on each visit. Most OB offices have an OB doctor, a nurse practitioner and a physician's assistant on staff, and together they will be the providers of your OB care. Some OB offices have a nurse midwife as well. Your OB visits are a top priority and so it is advisable for your husband to go with you as much as possible.

It is such a blessing to be pregnant. One way to acknowledge this awesome blessing is to say: Todah or thank you by adding one mitzvah (good deed) each time you have a prenatal doctor's appointment. By increasing your mitzvot (plural for mitzvah) with each month of pregnancy, you are adding not only to your own blessings but you are increasing the goodness in the world to which you are bringing a new life. What a wonderful gesture of gratitude that you can create! See page 164 in the Jewish life cycle section for more about The Value of Mitzvot.

# WHAT USUALLY OCCURS AT EACH OB VISIT

### 1. Weight

Your weight will be checked at each visit. Weight gain should be steady and gradual. An unexplained jump in your weight is of concern. The usual weight gain depends on your pre-pregnancy weight and other factors. The generally recommended weight gain during pregnancy is 25-30 pounds. It is important to monitor your weight, because sharp weight gain may be an indicator of pre-eclampsia, which will be discussed during the "Toxemia of Pregnancy" section.

### 2. Blood pressure

The normal parameters for blood pressure measurements are 140 or less for the systolic number (the upper number) and 90 or less for the diastolic number (the lower number). A systolic blood-pressure measurement that is less than 90 and diastolic measurement less than 60 are indications of possible concern and so should be checked regularly. In other words, during pregnancy, blood-pressure levels that are too high or too low can be a concern. Your blood pressure indicates how hard your heart is working. High blood pressure may be indicative of pre-eclampsia.

### 3. Abdominal measurements

The length of a full-term pregnancy is about 40 weeks or ten lunar months. After 20 weeks, the measurement in centimeters of your belly's size is approximately equal the number of weeks you are pregnant, give or take one to two centimeters. This measurement is taken from the pubic bone to the top of the fundus, which is the top of the uterus. When the fundal level (the top of the uterus) is at the umbilicus (the belly-button) you are considered to be approximately 20 weeks pregnant. This is sometimes referred to as the first "ski slope." When the height of the fundus is under the rib cage, you are approximately 40-weeks pregnant. This is known as the second "ski slope." The variations in measurement depend on the height of the pregnant woman, her weight gain, and the position and size of the baby.

### 4. Urinalysis
A urinalysis is done to determine the amount of sugar in the urine and to check for the possibility of diabetes. The urinalysis also checks for the presence of protein in the urine, a sign of pre-eclampsia or toxemia of pregnancy.

### 5. Fetal heart tones
After 10-12 weeks, fetal heart tones will be checked with a doppler, a special stethoscope. Normal fetal heart tones are usually between 120 to 160 beats per minute.

### 6. Leopold maneuvers
After 36 weeks, the doctor can estimate the size, position and presentation of the baby by externally palpating the shape of the woman's abdomen with his/her hands.

### 7. Edema
Edema (swelling) in the arms and legs and face, will be checked with each visit. Mild foot and ankle swelling is common at the end of pregnancy. However, marked edema may be indicative of pre-eclampsia. It is important to limit the salt added to your foods, avoid salty foods, and make sure that you are drinking 6-8 glasses of water per day.

## 8. Toxemia of Pregnancy

Five to eight percent of all pregnant women have toxemia of pregnancy, which is the hypertension of pregnancy. Check with your doctor about his/her guidelines regarding prevention of toxemia. Pre-eclampsia is considered the "calm before the storm." A pregnant woman with pre-eclampsia will often feel just fine. During the period of pre-eclampsia, there is often some edema, increased weight gain, high blood pressure or high levels of protein in the urine, but you do not need to have all of these symptoms to be considered in pre-eclampsia. Usually two out of the four of the above symptoms are indicative of pre-eclampsia. Severe pre-eclampsia has all of the above symptoms but they advance into severe headache, changed aura, a feeling of doom and gloom, nausea, vomiting, chest pain and ultimately seizures (eclampsia). If this happens, it is an emergency situation for you and the baby, and you need to contact your doctor immediately. With pre-eclampsia, you are often put on bed rest at home or in the hospital with IV medication in order to prevent you from moving into full-blown eclampsia. You may feel fine even when these pre-eclampsia symptoms are present. For this reason, it is vital to keep your regular prenatal visits. Depending on the severity of your symptoms and due date, delivery may be the best way to protect both you and your baby.

## 9. Gestational diabetes

Four percent of all pregnant women have gestational diabetes, which is high blood sugar levels during pregnancy. The glucose tolerance blood test is ordered to check for gestational diabetes. Your doctor will advise you when this lab test will occur and what preparation is required. Although gestational diabetes usually goes away after pregnancy, you have an increased risk for developing diabetes in the future. It is advisable to have a FBS (fasting blood sugar) test on a yearly basis to check for this. Prevention is best. Making healthy food choices, staying in the recommended weight range, and a doctor approved exercise regimen are some ways to help prevent gestational diabetes. If you do develop gestational diabetes, your doctor will advise you regarding special meal plans, monitoring your blood sugar level, and possible need for insulin injections.

# DANGER—WARNING SIGNS DURING PREGNANCY

It is essential that you are able to distinguish between normal changes of pregnancy and symptoms that are not normal. You should know how to reach your doctor 24 hours a day, seven days a week if you are unsure whether symptoms you are experiencing are normal or abnormal changes. Your OB will want to hear from you. Being prepared means knowing when you need professional help.

*If you experience any one of the following symptoms, call your doctor immediately:*

1. Bright red bleeding from the vagina, with or without cramps.
2. Persistent vomiting.
3. Sharp abdominal pain.
4. Persistent headaches.
5. Blurred vision or dots in front of the eyes.
6. Chills and fever.
7. Decrease in urinary output.
8. A gush or trickle of clear fluid from the vagina.
9. Significant decrease in fetal movement over a 24-hour period (after 24 weeks).
10. Any other symptom that you find worrisome.

Throughout your pregnancy, your doctor will provide you with specific instructions regarding your pregnancy, symptoms, concerns and techniques for monitoring your baby's movement. From the 28th week on, your doctor will likely advise you to monitor your baby's movements using a kick-count sheet. Check with your doctor how he/she wants you to monitor your baby's kick counts. This is vitally important.

# CHAPTER EIGHT

# Childbirth Medical Information

*"Relieving anxiety during your pregnancy can be done by testing early."*

## JEWISH GENETIC DISEASES AND TESTING

The following is a brief summary of some of the known Jewish genetic diseases. If you have any concerns regarding this topic, consult with your doctor. It is advisable to meet with a genetic counselor before you become pregnant or at the very beginning of your pregnancy.

Check with your doctor for a complete list of all Jewish genetic diseases. Ideally, it is wise to be tested before you get pregnant to see if you and/or your partner is a carrier of any Jewish genetic disease. Once you are already pregnant, early lab testing is recommended.

The Ashkenazi Jewish Genetic Panel (AJGP) is a blood test that screens for genetic diseases found more frequently in the Eastern European/Ashkenazi Jewish population. Test panels may differ from lab to lab, so check with your doctor or genetic counselor about the specific tests included in your AJGP panel.

### Ashkenazi Jewish Genetic Diseases

Certain diseases are more frequent in the Eastern European/Ashkenazi Jewish population. Diseases included in this group are often part of the AJGP panel.

When people think of Jewish genetic diseases they generally think of Tay Sachs disease, a disease which causes a buildup of fatty substances (gangliosides) in the cells of the brain and nervous system. Tay Sachs disease affects one in 900 Jewish couples. This is an avoidable genetic disease. Tay Sachs is included in the AJGP along with a number of other lesser known Jewish genetic diseases. It is not to say that these diseases are exclusive to the Ashkenazi Jewish population, but they are known to be more prevalent in this group.

### Sepharadic Jewish Genetic Diseases

There are genetic labs that test for Sepharadic Jewish genetic diseases, too. These genetic diseases are found more frequently in descendants from Spain, Portugal, the Mediterranean Sea area, and North Africa. These genetic diseases include Beta Thallassemia, Familial Mediterranean Fever, Glucose-6 Phosphate Dehydrogenase, and Type III Glycogen Deficiency Storage disease.

Relieving anxiety during your pregnancy can be done by testing early under the direction of a genetic counselor and your doctor.

# TERATOGEN PRECAUTIONS

A teratogen is any substance that can cause birth defects. It is important to avoid alcohol, tobacco, paint fumes, pesticides, drugs and second-hand smoke. Always check with your doctor regarding any over-the-counter medications, prescriptions, herbal supplements, inhalants, creams, and hair products., as they may be harmful to your baby. Pregnant women should stay away from cat litter. Ask your doctor about toxoplasmosis, a single-celled parasite that can be contracted when a pregnant woman is exposed to cat feces, often via cat litter. You will also want to be informed about other contagions that are of most concern when you are around small children, such as Fifth's Disease, Rubella, Roseola and Chickenpox. Check with your doctor regarding the safety of all immunizations. Always consult with your doctor if you are concerned about any kind of exposure. California Teratogen Information Service (CTIS) and Clinical Research Program has a special website at *www.ctispregnancy.org* to provide information about teratogens and pregnancy risk.

# THE RH FACTOR AND RHOGAM

One of the first tests you'll have, once you find out you're pregnant, is a blood-type test to determine your Rh factor. Most of the population, about 85%, is Rh positive and do not require any special follow-up or treatment. However, when the mother is Rh negative and the baby's father is Rh positive, a potential health problem for the baby could result. If the baby is Rh positive, the Rh negative mother's body will produce antibodies against the baby's Rh positive blood factor. This usually won't be a problem for the first pregnancy, but may be a problem for future Rh positive pregnancies. To protect future pregnancies from the antibodies, the Rh-negative mother of an Rh positive baby will be given a shot of immunoglobulin, also known as Rhogam, to prevent the production of antibodies. The shot is given at 28 weeks pregnant, again after the delivery, and for any future miscarriages or births. If the baby is Rh negative, there will be no reaction to the baby's Rh factor and so no Rhogam shot is necessary. The baby's blood type will be checked from the cord blood after the baby is born.

# HAVING AN ULTRASOUND

An ultrasound exam is done by sending low-intensity sound waves through the patient's body. The waves are reflected back and are received by the transducer. The sound waves are then translated onto an oscilloscope, forming a picture made up of electrical bleeps. Ultrasound in pregnancy can reveal information about the baby's gestational age and other facts about the baby.

Each doctor has his/her own ultrasound protocol. Generally speaking, at the first OB appointment, you usually have a limited ultrasound which is a pelvic sonogram. This may be done transvaginally (i.e., a vaginal probe is inserted). This is similar to having a pap smear. This is done when you are 8-10 weeks pregnant.

This test will not show the sex of the baby, but it can reveal the following information:
1. The location of the baby. The doctor can determine via ultrasound if the baby is in the uterus or if the pregnancy is in the fallopian tubes (an ectopic pregnancy). An ectopic pregnancy is an emergency situation.
2. Whether you are pregnant with one or more babies.
3. The gestational age of the baby which is determined by measuring the crown rump length (CRL) and the bi-parietal diameter ( BPD), the baby's head circumference.
4. The presence of cardiac action. In other words, you will be able to see the fetal heart motion of your baby.
5. The evaluation of the amount of amniotic fluid or the AFI (Amniotic Fluid Index).

The doctor may order repeat ultrasounds as needed to check the size, dates, and status of the baby.

At 18-20 weeks, you may have a formal ultrasound. You should arrive for your ultrasound appointment with a full bladder. You will lie on the exam table and gel will be applied to your abdomen. On the small screen, you can watch the electrical bleeps forming a picture as the transducer is placed over your abdomen. Often you will be given a printed picture to keep. The procedure takes 15-60 minutes, depending on the fetal activity and the baby's position.

> The following will be determined at the formal ultrasound:
> - The sex of the baby, if the sexual organs are in view.
> - The assessment of the liver, heart, kidneys, and brain
> - The size of the baby.
> - Any abnormalities with the baby.
> - Evaluation of the amount of amniotic fluid or the AFI (Amniotic Fluid Index).

At this ultrasound, if you choose to find out if your baby is a boy or a girl, you may start thinking about the baby's "Bris" or "Brit Milah" for a boy, and the Baby Naming ceremony for a girl.

# WHAT IS AMNIOCENTESIS?

This test can provide information about genetic disorders. This test is generally offered when there are concerns about a family history of a genetic disorder or for women who will be 35 years old or older at the time of their delivery. The test is usually done in the fourth month of pregnancy. It can also identify the gender of the baby. The amniocentesis results will inform the expectant parents about certain genetic disorders. They will be given valuable information regarding the status of their baby. Prior to the procedure, expectant parents will meet with a genetic counselor who will gather information about the families' medical history and provide support, guidance and information.

Under sterile conditions, a small amount of amniotic fluid via a needle is withdrawn from the amniotic sac through your abdomen. Sometimes, there is an increase in uterine activity following this procedure, but in most cases the uterus returns to normal within the hour. The physician or perinatologist, the specialist in maternal-fetal medicine who performs the amniocentesis, should explain all the risks, concerns and possible side effects prior to the procedure.

# OTHER TESTS

You may wish to talk with your doctor about being tested for GBS, or Group Beta Streptococcus infection. The CDC suggests that all women be tested at between 35 to 37 weeks of pregnancy. GBS is easily treatable and, although it is not generally serious in adults, it can be to newborns. If you are GBS positive, you will be treated with IV antibiotics intrapartum (during labor).

Your doctor will advise you regarding the best treatment of GBS as there are other parameters that will be evaluated.

# CHAPTER NINE

# Anatomy Basics

*"There is such a special sweetness in being able to participate in creation."*

## MALE GENITALIA

In the many years I've been teaching, I've discovered that many people haven't had the opportunity to learn exactly how a baby is conceived and how important the male anatomy is to this process. It's helpful to start with some basics in order to give a foundation upon which to learn. This brief overview is designed to enhance or add to your prior knowledge.

1. **Penis** – is the male sex organ.
   Each ejaculation contains approximately 300 million sperm. The sperm's life span is between 24 and 72 hours.

2. **Seminal vesicles** – holds the semen, which is a thick, viscid secretion discharged from the penis at orgasm, containing spermatozoa.

3. **Testes (testicles)** – produce the sperm.
   Men are fertile 24 hours a day. Testes are the counterpart to the ovaries in women.

**4. Scrotum** – holds and protects the testes.

In hot weather, they hang away from the body, and in cold weather they stay close to the body in order to maintain the sperm at an average temperature, a temperature at which the sperm can remain viable and active.

**5. Vas Deferens** – is the canal from which the sperm travel out of the penis through the urethra.

A vasectomy seals off this canal so that the sperm cannot pass through the urethra. Once a vasectomy has been performed, the sperm is reabsorbed into the body. Seminal fluid or semen is still produced and discharged but will no longer contain sperm.

**6. Prostate gland** – seals off the passage of urine during intercourse.

After the age of 40, men should have a prostate exam to ensure that their prostate is healthy. Later in life, the prostate gland can often become enlarged and should be monitored by a doctor.

# FEMALE GENITALIA

**1. Two ovaries** – house the thousands of female egg cells. These are the counterparts to the testes in the male.

**2. Two fallopian tubes** – transport the egg to the uterus.

**3. Uterus** – or womb is the hollow, muscular sac in a woman's lower abdomen that houses and protects the baby during pregnancy.

The pre-pregnancy uterus is the size of a fist and at full-term pregnancy the uterus is the size of a watermelon.

**4. Vagina** – is three to five inches in length, functions as a birth canal, organ for intercourse, and duct for menstrual contents.

**5. Cervix** – is the lower third of the uterus, the gateway into the vagina.

This is the area that opens up during labor. Effacement, which happens during labor, is the thinning of the cervix measured in percentages. Dilation is the opening of the cervix measured in centimeters. Effacement and Dilation will be discussed in more detail in later chapters.

**6. Fundus** – is the upper part of the uterus.

Contractions of the uterus during labor cause effacement and dilation of the cervix. The fundus of the uterus is massaged externally postpartum (after you give birth) by the nurse, in order to prevent postpartum hemorrhage.

# STRUCTURES SPECIFIC TO PREGNANCY

The following explains the normal pregnancy state and what is occurring inside your body:

**1. Placenta** – often referred to as the afterbirth, is the pancake-shaped organ from which the embryo receives nourishment from your body during pregnancy.

The placenta begins to develop with implantation, generally in the second or third week of pregnancy.

**2. Umbilical Cord** – The umbilical cord is a rope-like cord, attached to the placenta.

It contains two arteries and one vein, coming from the center of the placenta to the baby's umbilicus. Food and oxygen filter in through the placenta and are carried to the baby via the umbilical cord. The baby's waste products travel from the baby through the umbilical cord and then through the placenta to your bloodstream to be excreted by your kidneys and lungs. This process puts more demands on your body.

**3. Amniotic Sac** – a layer of membrane which forms approximately 12 days after conception and envelopes the baby in a sac of colorless amniotic fluid.

This sac is sometimes called the "bag of waters." At full-term, the amniotic sac contains approximately one quart of fluid. This fluid keeps the baby cushioned in a safe and insulated environment throughout your pregnancy. When your bag of water breaks, it is important to note the color, presence of odor, and quantity. Normal amniotic fluid is clear and odorless; if not, it could be indicative of a problem, so be sure to mention this to your doctor. When your water breaks, even if it looks normal, call your doctor immediately to get further instructions. Once your bag of water breaks, even if you are not experiencing contractions, you need to contact your doctor right away. This is one sign of labor and will be discussed in more detail in later chapters.

**4. Mucous Plug** – seals off the cervix so that no bacteria can enter the uterus from the vagina during pregnancy.

You will notice a pink-tinged mucous discharge towards the end of your pregnancy. This is a sign that labor will likely be starting within a few days; however, it is not cause for alarm, nor is it a reason to call your doctor.

**5. Effacement** – is the taking up, thinning, or shortening of the cervix during labor.

**6. Dilation** – is the expansion of the cervical orifice, the opening of the cervix.

**7. Pelvis** – is comprised of your two hipbones, the sacrum, and the coccyx (tailbone).

The pelvis does not get larger in pregnancy, but the joints do soften to allow for your growing baby.

**8. Round Ligaments** – are the fibrous cord-type ligaments attached to the fundal portion of the uterus.

When stretched by uterine growth, you may experience shooting pains in the groin and pubic area. The round ligaments are like suspenders holding up a pair of trousers.

**9. Utero-Sacral Ligament** – is attached to the sacral portion of your lower back.

As your baby grows, you may experience increased lower-back discomfort associated with this ligament.

# STAGES OF FETAL DEVELOPMENT

*"May you grow from strength to strength."*
—JEWISH SAYING

Understanding the stages of fetal development will increase your knowledge and decrease anxiety. It is also exciting for expectant parents to learn about the phenomena of fetal development.

- One week after implantation, the first period is missed, and the tiny embryo is the size of the head of a pin.

- At six weeks, the eyes, the arm and leg buds, the nose, and the mouth are beginning to develop. The spine is prominent, and the brain and nervous systems are the first major systems to be laid down.

- At six to seven weeks, cardiac action of the embryo can be visually observed via pelvic sonogram and trans-vaginal transducer.

- At three months, all major systems of the baby are formed. In the remaining months of your pregnancy, these systems will continue to develop as your baby grows. The first three months of pregnancy are crucial to your future infant. During your first three months of pregnancy, your first trimester, you should avoid all medications, pelvic or abdominal x-rays, alcohol, tobacco, and any nutritional products except those approved by your physician.

- At four months, your tiny baby is approximately eight to ten inches long and weighs six ounces. This is about the time you will experience "quickening." "Quickening" is the term that describes when you begin to feel your baby move for the first time. At this point in your pregnancy, your body begins to show visible signs of pregnancy.

- At six months, the fundus of the uterus has reached the height of your umbilicus. The baby is approximately 12 inches long and has downy hair and fingernails.

- At seven months, your baby could survive if it was born, but it would need a specialized environment of the NICU (the Neo-natal Intensive Care Unit). The lungs are still immature, the baby does not have a layer of fat for insulation to keep the body temperature constant, the facial and jaw muscles are not strong enough to suck, and there is very little resistance to infection.

- Nothing can match the perfect environment of a mother's womb. Whenever possible, it is best to reach a minimum of thirty-six weeks in utero. A baby delivered at thirty-seven to thirty-eight weeks is considered full-term.

- Pre-term labor is when your labor begins prior to the thirty-seventh week of pregnancy. If this occurs, the doctor may put you on bed rest and pelvic rest (no sexual intercourse or sexual stimulation by any means). The doctor may prescribe medications to be administered at home or at the hospital. Check with your doctor regarding pre-term labor precautions and guidelines. It is always important to be well hydrated and drink six to eight glasses of water per day to avoid dehydration. Also beware that too much water is not safe either. You should not drink more than 10 glasses of water a day, as this can "water down" your electrolytes and can lead to heart problems and seizures.

# DEFINING THE TRIMESTERS OF PREGNANCY

Each week of pregnancy presents an opportunity to add one more Jewish act to the expectant mother's and father's collection of Jewish experience. There is such a special sweetness in being able to participate in creation.

**First Trimester:**
Conception
14 weeks

**Second Trimester:**
14 weeks - 26 weeks

**Third Trimester:**
26 weeks - 40 weeks

# CHAPTER TEN

# Preparing for Labor and Delivery

*"Don't forget a pen and paper
to record progress in a journal."*

## CHILDBIRTH EDUCATION

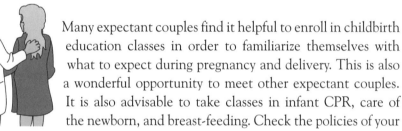

Many expectant couples find it helpful to enroll in childbirth education classes in order to familiarize themselves with what to expect during pregnancy and delivery. This is also a wonderful opportunity to meet other expectant couples. It is also advisable to take classes in infant CPR, care of the newborn, and breast-feeding. Check the policies of your hospital so that there will be fewer unknowns when you are actually in labor. Each hospital or birth facility is very individual. Here is a list of some suggested questions to ask:

- What are the admission procedures?
- What are the labor and delivery policies?
- What are the policies regarding videotaping?
- What are the postpartum procedures?
- What is the customary length of stay?
- What are the visiting hours and who is allowed to visit?

It is important to have a sense of teamwork among you, your coach, your doctor, and family. You may want to prepare a labor and delivery plan that includes medication, anesthesia, routine episiotomy, maternal/paternal infant bonding patterns, and any other factors regarding the birth experience that are important to you.

# WHAT TO TAKE TO THE HOSPITAL
## PACKING YOUR LABOR BAG

This bag will be filled with items you may need during labor. Suggested items include:

1. Remember your Shir La'maalot Birthing Card (See page 133. To receive your complimentary card please visit *www.lmazeltov.org*)
2. Lunch-size brown paper bag to help during hyperventilation.
3. Focal point (the object you practiced focusing on when doing your breathing exercises).
4. Pen and paper to record progress in a journal.
5. Scrunchies for your hair.
6. Socks.
7. Washcloths.
8. Battery-operated fan for your face.
9. Lip balm or lip gloss.
10. Toothbrush and toothpaste.
11. Pillows (two with bright-colored pillow cases, so they don't get lost at the hospital).
12. Deck of cards or any other table games.
13. Camera and film with batteries or charger for the camera.
14. Video camera and charger if your doctor allows.
15. List of phone numbers of friends and relatives.
16. Baby book so baby's footprints can be imprinted in it.
17. Watch with a second hand.
18. Unscented lotion or powder (strong aromas may cause nausea for the mother during labor).
19. Two tennis balls in a sock (for back labor).
20. Covered rolling pin or paint roller (for back labor).

21. Tart lollipops such as lemon (no loose candy; sweet lollipops tend to make you more thirsty).
22. Lunch and snacks for your coach (pack this last so that it will not spoil; not too spicy, also; beware that strong aromas may cause nausea for the laboring mom).

# YOUR SUITCASE

This suitcase will be filled with items for you, the mother, while you are recuperating in the hospital.
1. Robe.
2. Slippers.
3. Pajamas or nursing nightgown (to allow you to easily nurse your baby).
4. At least two bras (nursing bras if breastfeeding).
5. Breast pads.
6. Underwear.
7. Sanitary pads.
8. Toiletries.
9. Going home clothing—loose clothing (like a t-shirt or drawstring sweatpants).

# TAKE-HOME CLOTHING FOR YOUR BABY

*"wear it in good health."*
—JEWISH SAYING

1. An outfit for the new baby.
2. T-shirt.
3. 3-5 diapers.
4. Baby wipes.
5. Receiving blanket.
6. Outer blanket.
7. Outer outfit and a hat (if needed).
8. Car Seat.

# CHAPTER ELEVEN

# Breathing and Relaxation Techniques

*"The world is a narrow bridge and the most important part is not to be afraid."*
—RABBI NACHMAN OF BRETSLAV

## THE THEORY BEHIND BREATHING AND RELAXATION TECHNIQUES IN LABOR

Anticipating and experiencing pain can influence your level of anxiety. Fear of the unknown tends to increase your level of tension. One of the advantages of childbirth education is to learn techniques that will help you cope with the pain and anxiety that accompany labor.

Relaxation is the key to your comfort during childbirth. Even if you choose to use any kind of medication in labor or any regional anesthetic such as an epidural, it is important to learn how to relax in any case. If an epidural is part of your birth-plan, it may take many hours before you will be a candidate for one, making it important to learn both the breathing techniques and relaxation techniques. An epidural is not administered until you are well into labor (about three or four centimeters dilated with regular, consistently strong uterine contractions). This could take hours, so having other tools to reduce your discomfort is vital. You can read additional information about epidurals later in this book. The main purpose is to relax all the muscle groups that are not mandatory during labor. This will decrease your tension, fear and anxiety, since it will give more oxygen to the uterine muscle and it will decrease your pain. Total relaxation is not automatic but can be learned. In order to learn it well, it must be practiced.

Anxiety-reduction tools to help you cope with labor and delivery include: focused attention, breathing and relaxation techniques, and a greater understanding of the labor and delivery process. All these tools help inhibit the negative influences of anxiety and muscle tension, resulting in a smoother, more comfortable birth experience. Another way to relax is to add distraction. Sometimes, listening to calm music or a calm voice can distract you and help you to relax. There is something called the "fear-tension pain" cycle that comes into play when you are in an unfamiliar situation. If you have fears or anxiety about labor and delivery (and who doesn't?), your level of tension will grow, and the tension will increase your level of pain. Knowledge of the breathing and relaxation techniques, distraction, a circle of caring family and friends, prayers, and love will help decrease the fear-tension pain cycle.

## WHY IS IT IMPORTANT TO RELAX?

*"A smile is not a chore. It is an opportunity to feel good about ourselves."*
—YOAV NADAV

Tension is stressful emotionally and physically, and can deplete your energy levels. Decreasing the amount of stress you experience during labor will be beneficial to both you and your partner. Take the time to discover where you are most likely to hold tension. It can be difficult to relax, so it's a good idea to discuss with your labor buddy what relaxes you the most. This is a very individual experience. An honest and open discussion will promote intimacy and cohesion between the two of you. Your environment plays a significant role in your ability to relax, as well. Creating a relaxing environment can involve playing soft music, dimming the lights, turning off the television, as well as surrounding yourself with a small circle of supportive friends and/ or family. Work together with your partner as a team and practice relaxation on a regular basis to become familiar and comfortable with what relaxes each of you.

# ACHIEVING RELAXATION

**Note**: It is important to do your relaxation exercises when your bladder is empty. You do not want to be thinking, "oh, I need to go to the bathroom" when you're trying to relax. Also, wear loose clothing and be free of distraction.

Understanding the concepts of conserving your energy and oxygen will help you reduce your stress and help you relax during labor. Relaxation encourages better circulation, which enhances the oxygen balance in your body, a benefit to both you and your baby.

Practice improves your relaxation skills. The goal is to practice your relaxation techniques so that they become automatic.

To begin the relaxation process, you first need to be in a comfortable position—either sitting cross-legged with your elbows supported by pillows, or lying on your side with pillows under your head and between your knees so that no body part is resting on another body part.

# TOUCH RELAXATION

Tension can be released from the body through the use of touch or massage.

Coaches, try to be very gentle, patient and supportive when touching or massaging your partner. Make a strong effort to remain calm and patient, even if she becomes cranky. Avoid dropping an arm or leg or letting it hit the ground. Also, strive to be very gentle when handling parts of her body. You must be as relaxed as possible. Use a friendly, even tone when you are talking to your partner while she is in labor.

# A RECIPE FOR RELAXATION

During practice, I suggest that the coach practice the same relaxation techniques as the mother-to-be in order to have a better understanding of how it works.

Take your time; rushing to relax is counterproductive. As you begin the process of relaxation, your partner can start by checking your extremities, one at a time, for tension.

- Select one body part at a time.
- Take a deep breath. Slowly inhale and exhale.
- Tense the body part you have selected.
- Hold the tension for a few seconds.
- Gently relax the body part, allowing all the tension in your body to melt away.

The following is a recipe, an example of a concentrated relaxation exercise. You can use this as a guideline while creating your own relaxation techniques. The goal is to learn how to consciously relax specific muscle groups while others are contracted. You may want to be in a position where you are practicing in a side-lying position, sitting up or lying on your back with pillows to support your head and extremities. Always fold a pillow or blanket under your back so you are not completely flat on your back, but you are tilted to one side or the other. Try this relaxation technique for all parts of the body until the whole body is totally relaxed. Start with each arm, then each leg and then you may want to add your head, neck or tushie. For example, tense the muscles of your right leg and then relax. Tense the muscles of your left leg and then relax. Tense the muscles of your right arm and left leg and then relax. You can be creative in tensing and relaxing different areas of your body. If your partner should become impatient with you or use a loud voice to tell you to "hurry up and relax", it is time for a break. Resume practicing when you are both more relaxed. The tone of voice and body language must also communicate relaxation. Being too rough or ticklish will only increase tension. It is recommended to practice two to three times per week by yourself and once or twice per week with your partner.

# WHAT IS A FOCAL POINT?

During your labor contractions, you may find it helpful to have a focal point. Focusing your concentration on your focal point is a form of self-hypnosis.

A focal point can be anything that you look at, for example, your partner's face, your favorite stuffed animal, a colorful picture, or a rose in a vase. Looking at the focal point can help capture your concentration and allow you to experience less pain during a contraction. You can have multiple focal points.

# BREATHING TECHNIQUES — AN OVERVIEW

The goal of breathing techniques during labor and delivery is to 1) have an even exchange of air to prevent hyperventilation; 2) oxygenate the baby and your body; 3) provide a concentration stimulus and keep the diaphragm breathing muscle off the uterus; 4) create a state of relaxation; and 5) provide for pain reduction.

Don't be preoccupied with using techniques exactly like a book, instructor, or other people you know, unless it works well for you. You need to create your own atmosphere and your own way of coping. If the above criteria are met, then you are accomplishing these goals and you are doing a good job. If one breathing technique is not working for you, switch to another. It is okay to do whatever works best for you. Be aware that the breathing techniques may feel different during labor rehearsal versus the real labor.

You will generally begin with the slow-chest breathing. This and other breathing techniques will be described in detail beginning in the upcoming sections on Stages of Labor. All breathing techniques will begin and end with a deep cleansing breath. When a contraction begins, a cleansing breath will be the first step. This beginning cleansing breath is saying "it's time to focus and concentrate." The closing cleansing breath is saying that "I'm through; it's time to relax." Cleansing breaths are like bookends on a bookshelf, providing a defined beginning and end to your contractions. Focusing helps to distract you from the tightening of a contraction. The focal point can be a familiar object from home, anything that makes you feel comfortable.

# CHAPTER TWELVE

# Overview of Labor

*"Words of wisdom: Do not exhaust yourself. Pace yourself as you undertake the process of nesting."*

## UNDERSTANDING WHAT IS HAPPENING

Knowing what to expect during labor and delivery will lessen your anxiety about the process. Understand that each person's experience is a personal one and no two birth stories are ever the same. Even for the same person, no two labors are alike.

The usual length of labor for a first-time mother is 8 to 14 hours, and about half that amount of time for women who have given birth before. The amount of time in labor depends on the status of your cervix, the uterus, the intensity of the contractions, the position of the baby and the size of your pelvis.

Signs of labor are lightening or engagement, softening of the cervix, effacement and dilation, loss of the mucous plug, when your bag of water breaks, and uterine contractions that get longer, stronger, and closer together.

# LABOR — WHY DOES IT BEGIN?

*There are three main theories of why labor begins:*

**1. The Hormonal Theory** – Progesterone controls the length of pregnancy; therefore, as the end of pregnancy draws near, there is a decrease in the level of progesterone.

**2. The Fetal-Control Theory** – The baby secretes some substance that causes labor to begin.

**3. The Placenta Theory** – The placenta cannot continue to nourish the average seven-pound baby and this triggers your body to expel the baby at the end of pregnancy.

# HOW THE BODY PREPARES FOR LABOR

The following are some signs that the body is getting ready for labor:

**1. Engagement (or Lightening)** – Engagement is when the baby "drops." Engagement happens when the presenting part of the baby (usually the head) is descending into the birth canal. For primagravidas (a woman who is delivering for the first time) this usually occurs two to four weeks before delivery. For multigravidas (a woman who has previously delivered a child) this can take place anytime during the last few days of her pregnancy and can even occur during labor. After engagement, you may experience more pressure on your bladder because the baby is resting lower in your body. You may also be able to breath better now and have reduced reflux symptoms because the diaphragm (breathing muscle) now has more room to expand.

**2. Braxton-Hicks Contractions** – Braxton-Hicks contractions are false-labor contractions and are felt mostly in the abdominal area. These increase in frequency as you get closer to your due date. These contractions are fairly mild and irregular, and are not painful. They do not progress in terms of length, strength, or interval. Braxton-Hicks contractions soften the cervix so partial effacement may take place and some dilation is noted, especially in the multigravida.

**3. Mucous plug** – A mucous plug seals off the cervix so that no bacteria can enter the uterus from the vagina during pregnancy. Approximately one week before your due date, you may notice a pink- or brown-tinged mucous discharge. This is the mucous plug. You do not need to call the doctor or rush to the hospital. This is a sign that labor will likely be starting within a few days. Note: The mucous plug should not be bright red bleeding. If it is, call your doctor immediately.

**4. Rupture of membranes** – Rupture of membranes is the leakage or gush of amniotic fluid from the vagina. This is a warm rush of fluid which may occur before or during labor. Although the rupture of membranes is painless, you must call the doctor immediately. Once your "water breaks," it is a good idea to be delivering within 24 hours to prevent infection. You'll want to note the amount and color of the liquid, whether it is a gush or a leak, and differentiate between urine and amniotic fluid by the odor, color, and amount. Amniotic fluid is odorless and colorless. Urine is tinged yellow and smells like urine. You cannot stop the rush of the amniotic fluid, but you can stop the flow of urine by contracting your pelvic floor muscles. The body constantly produces more amniotic fluid, so there's no such thing as a "dry birth." Note: If the amniotic fluid is green in color, this is a sign that the baby has had a stool (meconium) and that the baby may be in distress. Call your doctor immediately.

**5. Nesting** – Nesting or great bursts of energy tend to occur as you move closer to your delivery day. It is natural to want to make your home ready for your expected offspring. Words of wisdom: Do not exhaust yourself. Pace yourself as you undertake the process of nesting. For example: Clean one closet at a time. Do not empty every closet as you may not have the energy to put it all back. By taking on one smaller project at a time, you can avoid leaving your house in a state of chaos or overwhelming yourself. Avoid fatigue by having rest periods during the day to save your energy for the stress of labor.

L'Mazeltov

# WHY INDUCE LABOR?

There are medical indications for induction of labor. Labor may be induced for a number of reasons, including the premature rupture of membranes, toxemia, gestational diabetes (diabetes that occurs only during the pregnancy state), hypertension (high blood pressure) and prolonged pregnancy. Your physician will evaluate your status and determine if you need to have your labor induced.

The following are methods to induce labor:

**1. Nipple stimulation** – There is some evidence that shows that stimulation of the nipples can begin labor. Nipple stimulation can be done with the use of a breast pump, or by manual or oral stimulation. Nipple stimulation releases the secretion of the natural Oxytocin in your body which causes your uterus to contract. You will notice that uterine contractions will also occur postpartum, after your delivery, when you breastfeed your infant. These contractions are referred to as "after pains." They help the uterus to contract down to its small size after the baby is born. Some doctors are advocating the trial use of breast stimulation before attempting induction of labor by Pitocin.

**2. An amniotomy** – An amniotomy is the artificial rupture of membranes. The amniotomy or breaking of the bag of waters is done with an amniohook. The phrase breaking of the bag of waters or the term amniohook make it sound like this procedure would be very painful, but it is not. The procedure simply involves a basic vaginal exam where the doctor gently nicks the bag of waters to begin or augment the process of labor. It is important to note that once the bag of waters breaks, the doctor is evaluating the color of the amniotic fluid to determine if it is clear and odorless. A doctor may decide to perform an amniotomy, usually after you are at least two to three centimeters dilated.

**3. Oxytocin/Pitocin induced labor** – Oxytocin is the same as Pitocin. Oxytocin occurs naturally in your body, whereas Pitocin is the synthetic version of the hormone. Pitocin is infused into the woman's forearm through an intravenous IV line. Contractions that are induced or augmented by Pitocin are often stronger and occur with more frequency. Contractions can be regulated easily by speeding up or slowing down the rate of the Pitocin infusion. Pitocin may be used to augment labor if the contractions are becoming ineffective. The infusion of Pitocin will also stimulate the release of your body's own natural Oxytocin. You should know that the induction of Pitocin does not always cause cervical dilation; it depends on how ripe the cervix is for induction. A ripe cervix is one that shows some effacement or thinning of the cervix, and is beginning to dilate (open). The Pitocin-induced contractions often cause stronger contractions and you must be prepared to be using your breathing and relaxation techniques perhaps a bit earlier than if you were to go into labor on your own naturally. Your doctor will discuss with you whether the use of Pitocin is right for your situation.

## TRUE LABOR VERSUS FALSE LABOR

Understanding the difference between true labor and false labor (Braxton-Hicks contractions) will increase your awareness of the laboring state, giving you valuable insight to differentiate whether you are actually in labor or not. Contractions are the means by which labor and delivery occur. False labor is not painful and is felt mostly in the abdomen. It is irregular, stops when you do an activity, and is mild in intensity. A true labor contraction is an intermittent tightening of the muscles of the uterus. These contractions can be felt near the pubic bone and radiate to the groin, thigh, and/or lower back. The nature of the contraction is involuntary: you cannot start it or stop it. There are rest periods in between contractions. This is an important time so that the placenta can replenish itself with fresh blood supply. A contraction is like a powerful wave. Learning breathing and relaxation techniques can enable you to ride the contraction with dignity. A true labor contraction is longer in duration, stronger in intensity, occurs more frequently, and does not go away. When in doubt, call your doctor.

# PARTNER SUPPORT DURING LABOR

*"To smile at your neighbor is more important than to offer him a drink."*
—TALMUD

The following are some of the ways your partner can support you when true labor contractions begin:

1. Start timing the contractions to determine how long the contractions last and how many minutes occur between the contractions. Your partner will time the contractions from the beginning of one contraction to the beginning of the next contraction, including the rest period between the contractions. Your partner can use a note pad to record the course of your labor by tracking the contractions. You do not have to time every single contraction in early labor. The goal is to get an idea of a pattern. To avoid fatigue, you will want to hold off using your breathing techniques until you cannot walk, talk, or laugh during a contraction.

2. The birthing partner can feel the contraction by gently palpating or touching the fundus (the top of the uterus) externally. It should feel very hard (like your forehead) during the contraction and soft (like the tip of your nose) during the rest periods.

3. In early labor you may want to take a nap, read, watch TV or take a shower, if your membranes have not ruptured and your contractions are mild and infrequent. If you can sleep through your  contractions, you do not need to time them. Avoid getting "burned out" by timing contractions too early in the game. As always, your doctor will be your best guide in determining what's best for your situation.

4. You may find that you are experiencing some ambivalent feelings as your contractions begin. Emotionally you are very excited, but you may also find that the reality of the labor, delivery and birth feel

overwhelming. Having your partner by your side will help you cope with these feelings.

5. Drink only clear fluids, since digestion slows down during labor. Herbal tea with honey is a good supplier of both fluid and energy. Other examples of a clear liquid are anything you can see through such as gelatin, chicken broth, apple juice, lemon-lime soda. Stay away from any dairy products. A milk shake is not a clear liquid!

6. When you are doing your breathing and relaxation techniques, you may want to make some changes along the way. There is a quote, "keep doing the same thing and you will get the same results." If your breathing techniques and relaxation techniques are not working well for you, it is okay to change the course in the middle and readjust your methods to help yourself cope with your labor. You may want to change your focal point. It is important for your coach to multi-task when helping you during labor. Your coach might need to give you a wet washcloth, fan you, breath with you, put socks on your feet, and give you a kiss on your cheek! Be sure to ask for what you need, as your coach cannot read your mind!

# EXTERNAL AND INTERNAL FETAL MONITORS

External and internal fetal monitors show the frequency and duration of a contraction, the quality of the fetal heartbeat and the efficiency of a placenta. A readout strip comes out of the machine, giving the medical staff vital information on the status of your baby.

The external monitor has two transducers attached to the abdomen with belts. One transducer is placed where the heartbeat of the baby is heard, and the other is placed at the fundus (top of the uterus) to measure the frequency and duration of the contractions. The external monitor is more cumbersome than the internal monitor in that it restricts the mother's ability to move about freely. You may need the nurse's assistance in unplugging the connection to the machine. The external fetal monitor is a more general type of monitor that can be used prior to labor and in early labor before the membranes are ruptured. The external monitor can only provide information regarding the frequency and duration of the contractions, not the actual strength of the contractions.

The internal fetal monitor consists of a scalp electrode that is passed through the mother's cervix and attached to the baby's head during a pelvic exam. Before the internal monitor can be used, the bag of waters must be ruptured and you will need to be at least three centimeters dilated. The internal monitor gives information about your contractions and the baby's heartbeat, whereas the IUPC (the Intrauterine Pressure Catheter) measures the strength, frequency and duration of your contractions.

This technology is very helpful but it is not the main focus of the birth experience.

---

### NOTE TO BIRTHING COACH

You can use the monitor to let your partner know that a contraction is beginning or ending, or when the contraction is peaking, but make sure you make your partner your main focus, not the monitor. Sometimes the monitor may not reflect the intensity of her contraction, and it may need to be adjusted by the nurse or doctor.

---

# CHAPTER THIRTEEN

# Problems during Labor and Delivery

*"Always follow your doctor's advice in all matters related to your pregnancy, labor and delivery."*

## SIX MAIN PROBLEM CATEGORIES

### 1. Problems with the passage (i.e. the pelvis)

This is when the baby cannot move though the birth canal due to cephalopelvic disproportion (CPD). Cephalopelvic disproportion is when the presenting part, the baby's head, does not engage or descend into the pelvis as labor progresses. In simple terms, the passage is too small for the baby's head.

### 2. Problems with the passenger (i.e. the baby)

A common problem with the passenger is when the position or size of the baby prevents the baby from passing through the birth canal. This can happen when the baby's size is too large in relation to your pelvis. Another situation would be if the head is poorly flexed or is extended, keeping in mind that the broadest diameters must pass through the pelvis. In addition, a position where the baby is lying sidewise or is in breech presentation (buttocks or footling breech) would most likely result in a cesarean section.

### 3. Powers of labor

Powers of labor refers to the intensity of the uterine contractions. Prolonged labor due to dysfunctional contractions is categorized as hypotonic or hypertonic. Hypotonic contractions are contractions that don't exert enough force to make changes in the cervix. This often happens when you are in labor for a long time. Pitocin may be introduced intravenously, which is referred to as "augmentation of labor," similar to the induction of labor discussed earlier. Hypotonic contractions generally respond well to stimulation by Pitocin.

Hypertonic Contractions—Hypertonic means that the uterine contractions are too strong, occur too frequently, are not coordinated and the uterus is not able to have a rest period between contractions. Hypertonic contractions are the result of hyper-stimulation of the uterus which may be caused by too much Pitocin. In this case, the Pitocin will need to be reduced. If the contractions are not due to the Pitocin level, the doctor will generally use medication to reduce the uterine hyper-stimulation. Hypertonic contractions can exhaust the mother and contribute to other complications.

### 4. Placenta Previa

Placenta Previa is a condition when the placenta is covering the cervix in the lower part of the uterus. Generally, during delivery the baby would come out of the uterus first, followed by the placenta. In this case, the placenta presents first. This is characterized by painless, bright red vaginal bleeding. If this should occur, lie down horizontally and call your doctor immediately. With Placenta Previa, you will likely have a cesarean section, depending on whether it is a partial or complete placental presentation.

### 5. Abruptio Placenta

Abruptio Placenta is when the placenta prematurely detaches from the uterine wall. The placenta normally remains attached to the wall of the uterus until the baby is delivered. Contributing factors for Abruptio Placenta can include trauma to the abdomen, certain medical conditions, and illicit drug use. This condition is characterized by a painful tightening of the abdomen where the abdomen can feel hard like a board and the tightening does not resolve. Abruptio Placenta is accompanied by copious (large amount) of bright red bleeding. This is an emergency situation and will generally result in an emergency cesarean section. Check with your doctor during one of your regular visits regarding the best way to respond to this condition. You may be instructed to call 911.

### 6. Precipitous labor

Precipitous labor is defined as a labor lasting three hours or less. This is common in multigravidas. If this is the case, the doctor may consider inducing labor to allow for a more controlled birth. For a woman with a history of precipitous delivery, adequate arrangements should be made to ensure a safe birthing experience.


# BACK LABOR

The most common variation of the first stage of labor is "posterior" or back labor—that is a labor in which you experience most of your discomfort in your back. This incident occurs in 30% of all labors.

Back labor is caused by the baby's posterior presentation, which is when the baby's head is down and is often referred to as being "sunny-side up." The baby's face in this case is presenting facing up, rather than the base of the baby's head. Consequently, the hard part of the baby's head is against the mother's spine, rather than the baby's soft face. This causes a labor that is felt as a dull ache or a boring sensation felt in the back and the legs, and may not completely disappear between contractions. The posterior presentation is more difficult because the uterine contractions are working to turn the baby's head as well as dilate the cervix. Back labor may result in a longer labor. The following are techniques for coping with back labor. Always consult with your doctor and follow your doctor's advice in all matters related to your pregnancy, labor and delivery.

1. **Get the baby and the pressure off the back by using these various positions:**

   a. A side-lying position—lie on the side where the baby's back is.
   b. Sitting cross-legged with pillows supporting your arms.
   c. Positioning on your hands and knees during contractions, doing a pelvic rock on all fours between contractions.
   d. Assuming a knee-chest position.
   e. Change your position frequently—every 30 minutes to one hour.

2. **Experiment with various temperature changes over the sacrum (the low back) to alleviate discomfort.**

Some women prefer warm and some women prefer cold. Experiment to see what works best for you. You can use a plastic hollow rolling pin filled with warm water, a warm blanket, a warm wet washcloth, or a heating pad. You can also use a cold pad, ice chips in your rubber gloves, washcloths in icy water, blue ice, or a plastic hollow rolling pin filled with ice and rolled onto the back. Keep in mind that ice can burn and stick to the skin. Always wrap an ice-filled object in a washcloth. Never use dry ice.

3. **Your coach can apply counter pressure to the area of discomfort.**

This is where they would apply a moderate, steady firm pressure to your lower back.

---

### COACH

Support your partner's hip while applying counter-pressure; otherwise, you will push your partner right off the bed. You can use a tennis ball inside a sock, a paint roller, or a rolling pin. You can do a gentle back massage or effleurage between contractions. You can use a lotion or a powder when performing counter-pressure or effleurage.

---

## YOU

You can do slow chest breathing between contractions and check carefully for tension using touch relaxation. It's important to consciously relax the back. When you have back labor, you may need to advance your breathing techniques sooner, so practice all the previously-learned breathing techniques and practice different sequences of pant blow breathing techniques with and without effleurage.

# CHAPTER FOURTEEN

# Anesthesia Overview and Descriptions

*"Knowledge gives you a realistic view of all your options."*

## TYPES OF ANESTHESIA

The advantage for couples who practice breathing techniques and are informed of what to expect in the birthing process is that they often need less medication during labor and delivery. Childbirth breathing and relaxation techniques provide their own form of analgesia. Prepared expectant mothers may need some medication, but usually a minimal amount. Some people may opt to use these techniques early in labor and then still use the epidural regional anesthetics in the later stage of labor. Studies have shown that having a coach present shortens the length of labor and decreases the amount of pain medication required. Some medications pass through the placenta to the baby and possible side effects to the infant depend on when medication is given, the amount administered, and what kind of medication is used. Timing is very important. Have a conversation with your doctor regarding your options for medication and possible side effects to your baby.

In this section, a variety of anesthesia options are discussed as an overview. Additional details can be provided by your physician so that you are fully informed of all benefits and risks related to each medication and procedure.

The following are categories of medication:

- **Analgesics** – This class of medication includes Tylenol and Ibuprofen and is usually taken orally for mild to moderate pain, and for fever reduction.

- **Narcotics** – One common narcotic medication used during labor is Stadol, although there may be other medications that your doctor may prescribe. Narcotic medications can stop or slow down labor and take the edge off the contractions. With the use of this category of medication, you may be able to sleep in between contractions. These are usually administered through an IV, and may cause you to relax and dilate more if given at the right time. Some side effects are nausea, vomiting, itchiness, confusion, or a sense of euphoria or apathy. Timing is very important, as the effects on the baby are more profound if given less than one hour before delivery. In addition, narcotics given via an IV can cross the placenta and make the baby sleepy at birth.

- **Tranquilizers** – Phenergan and Vistaril are antihistamines that have a sedating and calming effect. They may also be used during labor to counteract nausea caused by the narcotics. In addition, they are usually given with the narcotics because they potentiate the effectiveness of the narcotics. Tranquilizers, however, can

*L'Mazeltov*

cause lower blood pressure, which will need to be continuously monitored throughout your labor.

- **Barbiturates** – Your doctor will select the best options for your situation. This class of medications may be prescribed when the woman is in early labor and not progressing. Barbiturates can help a woman in early labor get a good night's sleep. Once she has regained her energy, the doctor may decide to induce labor the next morning. Possible side effects of this class of medication may include a slight amnesia effect, low blood pressure or dizziness.

- **Regional Anesthetics** – Regional anesthesia is a broad category of anesthetic medication that is injected directly into a specific area of the body. Common regional anesthetics used in labor include the epidural, spinal, local anesthetic, pudendal block and the paracervical block. The most common of them is the epidural. Most of you have heard about the "magical" epidural and are probably eager to learn more about it, so we'll start with a discussion of the epidural.

    1. **Epidural** – The epidural is extremely effective in relieving pain during labor. With the use of an epidural, you will remain alert and can basically relax, watch TV and take a nap while your cervix dilates. Eighty percent of all women get an epidural these days. The epidural will allow you to actively participate in the birthing process without becoming exhausted. The downside of having an epidural is that it can take up to 30 minutes from the time the procedure begins until you experience relief. An epidural can reduce sensation and you may not feel a strong urge to push. As a result, the amount of medication infused through the epidural catheter may be reduced to make your pushing efforts more effective. An epidural does not pass through the placenta and does not affect the baby's level of alertness at birth. As with all aspects of your pregnancy, labor and delivery, you

will want to discuss this and all anesthetic options with your doctor. Placement of the epidural generally causes minimal discomfort. The epidural placed in your lower back while you are sitting up or lying down on your side with your back arched "like a cat." Then your back will be prepped (washed with an antiseptic solution). The anesthesiologist will numb the area with a local anesthetic and then the epidural needle will be inserted into your lower back. The needle is inserted below the spinal cord and does not touch the spinal cord. The epidural catheter will be threaded into the epidural space (put in place via the needle) and the needle will be removed. The catheter is then secured and taped to your back. This will allow for a continuous epidural, the continuous administration of the medication through the catheter and can be started when a woman is about three to four centimeters dilated. A little catheter, like a thin tube of pasta, will remain in your back and the anesthesiologist can add more medicine through the catheter as your contractions get stronger. Once you have the epidural in place, you will need to stay in bed.

2. **Spinal Anesthesia** – Spinal anesthesia is a form of regional anesthesia that will completely numb you from the waist down. It involves the injection of the anesthetic directly into the cerebrospinal fluid. Spinal anesthesia, injected into the lower back, can be used for a vaginal delivery, especially when forceps or a vacuum are needed, or for a cesarean section and lasts one to two hours, whereas a continuous epidural provides relief during labor.

3. **Local Anesthesia** – Local anesthesia is an anesthetic medication that is administered into a defined area to numb that specific part of the body. During labor and delivery, a local anesthetic may be administered to numb your back before the epidural is placed and may also be used to numb the perineum during a vaginal delivery.

4. **Pudendal Block** – A pudendal block may be used to numb the pudendal nerves in the region of the vulva and labia majora.

5. **Paracervical Block** – A paracervical block may be used to numb the cervix during delivery. This type of regional anesthesia is used less frequently.

### General Anesthesia

Another category of anesthesia is general anesthesia. This is generally administered with an intravenous line. With general anesthesia, you will be completely unconscious. This is used for an emergency cesarean section when the baby needs to be delivered very quickly, generally due to fetal distress, and if the patient does not already have an epidural in place.

When you go for your prenatal visits, ask your doctor what types of anesthesia are available to you. The more information you have, the more empowered you will be when it comes time to deliver your baby. Knowledge gives you a realistic view of all your options. You are not a failure if you decide to take any sort of medication. Avoid feeling that you are less of a woman or that you are not "tough enough." Even though childbirth is a wonderful experience, it is not an easy one. I took childbirth education classes thirty years ago when I was pregnant with my first child. The instructor never used the word "pain." As a result, I felt that either everyone else didn't experience pain during childbirth or, if they did, they managed better and I was a "wimp." All of these modern technologies are designed to assist you in having the best possible birthing experience, and are considered to be relatively safe.

# CHAPTER FIFTEEN

# Three Stages of Labor: An Overview

*"Your main focus should be on controlled relaxation."*

## STAGE 1

**Stage 1** has three phases: early labor, active labor, and transition. During stage 1, the cervix begins the process of effacement and dilation. Effacement is thinning of the cervix, and dilation is the opening of the cervix. Stage 1 is the longest stage. At full dilation, the cervix is at 10 centimeters (the diameter of a softball) and this marks the end of stage one. At this point, the dilated woman is ready to push. During early labor, the cervix is dilated from zero to three centimeters and in active labor the cervix is dilated from four to seven centimeters. During transition, the cervix is dilated from eight to ten centimeters.

## STAGE 2

**Stage 2** begins when the woman is completely dilated to 10 centimeters and ends with the birth of the baby. This stage can last from a few minutes up to two hours or more, often depending on whether the mother has previously delivered a baby. It is during this stage that an episiotomy may or may not be performed.

# STAGE 3

Stage 3 begins after the birth of the baby and ends with the expulsion of the placenta. If an episiotomy has been performed, the episiotomy repair usually occurs at the end of this stage. Complete repair can take anywhere between 10 to 30 minutes. The issue of episiotomy will be discussed in more detail later in this book.

## ■ STAGE 1, PHASE 1 — EARLY LABOR: DETAILED DESCRIPTION

- Effacement is 50-75% percent.
- Dilation is 0-3 centimeters.
- Contractions occur every 5-20 minutes, lasting 30-60 seconds.

### YOU

You may feel excited, eager, apprehensive, uncertain and thrilled, and ambivalence is very common. Your role is to conserve energy, time your contractions, take in only clear liquids, empty the bladder every two hours, and start slow chest breathing when you cannot walk, talk, or laugh through a contraction. You can add a gentle massage, called effleurage, of the abdomen when it is needed.

### COACH

As the birthing partner, you can add a gentle massage, called effleurage, of the abdomen when she asks you. Your role is to rest or sleep, eat a full meal, and help her to relax, offer diversion, notify the doctor, time the contractions and keep a labor log. Remind her to empty her bladder (as she may forget!), support her efforts, coach her through her breathing techniques, reinforce the focal point, do effleurage if it is comfortable for her, encourage her and enjoy this special time together.

### NOTE

Effleurage is the massaging of the abdomen with the fingertips using a very gentle, delicate touch while moving the fingers in circular motions across the woman's belly. Be gentle, no pressure or tickling. It is not like kneading dough! Effleurage can be done by the woman in labor or by her coach.

### Early in Labor – For Her

It is important early in labor to have clear liquids, which is anything you can see through—for example, water, herbal tea, apple juice, lemon-lime soda, chicken broth, or gelatin. Avoid red or purple juices and gelatin. Digestion stops or slows down completely in labor. Milk products are not advised because they are hard to digest.

### Early in Labor – For Coaches

Eat a nice meal to fortify yourself before the big event. Avoid eating right in front of your partner, because she will be hungry. Avoid spicy foods and anything with garlic, as the smell may make her feel nauseated. Bring nutritious snacks. Bear in mind that, "a hungry coach is a lousy coach." Be well fed so you can give 100% attention to your laboring partner.

# BREATHING TECHNIQUES

## Slow Chest Breathing

Slow-chest breathing is generally used during early labor. Begin the slow-chest breathing only when you need it. Slow-chest breathing should be approximately 6-9 breaths per minute. This breathing technique is the least fatiguing and you can use it as long as it works for you.

The coach will say "contraction begins." You will then take a deep cleansing breath in and out, which is three seconds of air in and three seconds of air out. You can breathe in through your nose or your mouth, whichever is most comfortable for you. Generally, you would inhale through your nose and exhale through your mouth. After your initial cleansing breath, you will stare at your focal point and breathe in for four seconds and breathe out for four seconds, continuing for the entire duration of the contraction. When your coach says "contraction's over," you will take another cleansing breath in and out, and relax.

You may add mild effleurage at this point during labor. You can lightly massage with your fingertips over the abdomen, pubic bone area, legs or anywhere you would like. Some people find effleurage very pleasurable, while others don't like it all. You can use a mildly scented powder or cornstarch also during the massage.

To be prepared, practice your breathing techniques regularly at home, beginning in your sixth or seventh month of pregnancy, until you deliver. During your practice sessions, it may be helpful for your coach to call out 15-second increments to simulate the beginning, middle and end of a contraction, in order to provide more structure for your practice session. For example: Your coach may say, "contraction begins." At this point, you will take your cleansing breath, in and out, and proceed with your slow-chest breathing. While you are doing your slow-chest breathing, your coach will call off "15 seconds," "30 seconds," and "45 seconds" using a stopwatch or a watch with a second hand. After 45 seconds, the coach will say, "contraction over," at which time you will again take a cleansing breath, in and out. At this point, after the contraction, you will do your relaxation techniques.

During labor, you should change your position every half hour to one hour in order to promote better circulation for you and the baby. When in labor, avoid lying flat on your back, as this position compresses your major blood vessels and compromises blood circulation to the baby. Lying on your back can also make you feel dizzy, light-headed, or nauseated. The left-side lying position is the position of choice because it takes the pressure off your back and enhances blood circulation to the baby. This position also allows you and your coach to maintain good eye contact. It's okay to rest on your right side or to sit cross-legged, as well. In some hospitals, walking or standing during labor is restricted, especially if your water has broken. Semi-reclining with a tilt to the right or left is a good position for labor.

## STAGE 1, PHASE 2 — ACTIVE LABOR: DETAILED DESCRIPTION AND BREATHING TECHNIQUES

- Effacement is 75-100%.
- Dilation is 4-7 centimeters.
- Contractions are occurring every 2-4 minutes, lasting 45-60 seconds, and they are moderate to strong intensity.

The good news is that you may have your epidural in by now!

---

### YOU

You may begin to get serious and have the need to concentrate. You may also be nervous and uncomfortable and feel lonely. Your role is to conserve your energy and start slow chest breathing when necessary, if not already started. The following gives you tools to cope with whatever kind of labor you have. Walk if you feel up to it; check with the hospital policy. Empty the bladder every two hours; change your position often. Believe in yourself; advance

---

to the shallow chest breathing and accelerated/decelerated breathing when needed. Add effleurage as needed or desired. Completely relax and rest between contractions to conserve your energy.

## COACH

Your role as the birthing partner is to talk to her and encourage her. You will also be timing her contractions and keeping a labor log. During the labor, you will reinforce concentration and relaxation using touch relaxation, and you will be monitoring her breathing, and breathing with her if necessary.

As the coach, you will be providing comfort measures such as offering ice chips and lip balm, giving back rubs, arranging the pillows, doing effleurage and applying counter pressure to her back. The coach will also serve as the mediator between her and the hospital staff. Be sure to bring a lunch so you can stay with her during her labor (unless she asks you to leave while you're eating).

# SHALLOW CHEST BREATHING

Begin and end the shallow chest breathing with a cleansing breath. You can use the sound of "he, he" or, to prevent dryness of the mouth, you can use "she, she." You take your cleansing breath in and out and this is a signal that your concentration is beginning. The shallow chest is a more superficial breathing that keeps the diaphragm breathing muscle off the uterus, reducing pressure on the uterus, and decreasing discomfort during a contraction.

When a contraction begins, take a cleansing breath in and out, and then begin your shallow chest breathing. When the coach says "contraction begins," inhale, exhale crisply. Make the "she, she" or "he, he" sound. While breathing, maintain equal exchanges of air.

Vary a 45-60 second contraction, call out intervals of "15 seconds, 30 seconds, 45 seconds, contraction's finished" with a stopwatch or second hand watch. You may add effleurage during the contraction, along with the breathing techniques, if desired.

When a contraction declines, decrease the rate of your breathing. The coach says, "contraction's over," cleansing breath and relax. A cleansing breath means "I'm through" and it's time to relax.

Practice regularly at home, at least two shallow chest breathing with and without effleurage.

# HYPERVENTILATION

Hyperventilation occurs when there is an imbalance of oxygen and carbon dioxide in the body due to an increase in the rate or depth of respirations, or both. This is uncomfortable for you, and it can also cause distress to the baby.

When you do your breathing techniques, you need to have equal exchanges of air and it is important not to over-breathe (breathing too fast) in your practice sessions. Hyperventilation occurs more frequently during practice than during actual labor. During labor, the uterus uses great amounts of oxygen, so hyperventilation is less likely to occur. Your coach can hyperventilate also if he or she is not familiar with these breathing patterns. It is important for you and your coach to learn the breathing techniques in order to prevent hyperventilation for both of you. Hyperventilation can be prevented by pacing your breathing to ensure proper air exchange. It is helpful for the coach to breathe along with you to help you keep your breathing on track.

Symptoms of over-breathing are: dizziness; stars before the eyes; prickliness around the mouth and face; tingling in the fingers, hands or toes; feeling confused, anxious or tense; or your breathing patterns are off. To alleviate these symptoms, you need to restore the proper balance of oxygen and carbon dioxide in the body. The following can help you restore that balance:

- Cup your hands over your nose and mouth and breathe your own carbon dioxide during and between contractions;
- Breathe into a small paper bag;
- Hold your breath for a count of ten between contractions, which will build up carbon dioxide; or
- Clench your fists tightly causing tenseness in the muscles, thereby using excess oxygen between the contractions.

When controlled, hyperventilation will not be harmful to the baby, but prevention is best. Hyperventilation more often occurs to women that are not totally relaxed, so relaxation is the best antidote to hyperventilation.

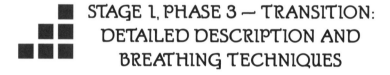

# STAGE 1, PHASE 3 — TRANSITION: DETAILED DESCRIPTION AND BREATHING TECHNIQUES

Transition is the hardest, but shortest, stage of labor. It is the bridge between contractions and expulsion—which is when you're giving birth.

- Effacement is 100%.
- Dilation 8-10 centimeters.
- Contractions are very strong with multiple peaks occurring every one to three minutes or one contraction occurring right after the other lasting 60-90 seconds or even as long as 120 seconds.

### Signs of Transition
Keep in mind that you will not feel most of transition if you have your epidural in place.

The following are signs of transition that you may experience.

> ## YOU
>
> You may experience some or all of the following: increased bloody vaginal discharge, nausea or vomiting, belching, hiccups, chills, hot flashes, profuse perspiration, trembling, not wanting to be touched, sense of failure, wanting to quit or wanting medication. You may also feel the urge to push.
>
> During transition you may feel irritable, discouraged, disoriented, irrational, scared, angry, withdrawn, restless, panicky, and tense. Your concentration will be impaired, and you will lose sense of time, space, and orientation.
>
> Your main focus should be on controlled relaxation. It's important, but very difficult. You can use your coach as a focal point, but do not push until you're given permission. When you push too soon, you can cause the cervix to swell up, therefore slowing things down. Also, pushing too early puts pressure on the baby's head, which can cause the cervix to become edematous (swollen) and or "molding" of the baby's head. Molding is when the baby's head takes the shape of a "cone head," which is temporary.
>
> Take one contraction at a time. This is the shortest phase of labor and it will soon be over. Concentrate on breathing techniques. Use straight blowing to control an urge to push. Relax in between contractions; you may need to use slow chest breathing between contractions.
>
> ## COACH
>
> It is your job to notify the nurse when you recognize the signs of transition. When you speak with your partner in labor, you should be very direct, supportive and gentle, reminding her to take one contraction at

a time. Breathe with her, if necessary, while pacing her breathing. Change the pattern of breathing, by breathing a bit faster, for very intense contractions, being careful not to hyperventilate. Establish eye contact with your partner and count off the length of the contractions at 15-second intervals. It's helpful to provide what's called "verbal analgesia" in your voice to help her to relax during this very difficult phase. Verbal analgesia means you should speak softly and kindly to her.

If she loses control of her breathing, be gentle but help her get back on track without yelling or blaming. If you cannot handle that, let someone else take over. Remember! She is the one in pain!

Consider the comfort measures: offer warm blankets if she's cold, or a cool washcloth for her brow, lips, and the back of her neck if she's warm. Have a little emesis (i.e., plastic, kidney-shaped) basin ready in case she feels nauseated. Encourage her and keep reminding her how close she is to giving birth. Never leave her alone during the transition phase of labor. Remind her not to push until she is given permission. It is crucial that you stay calm yourself, keep your labor log, and don't remind her or joke later about the things she said or did during transition!

### How to Help Your Partner Regain Control

Hold her face in your hands and establish eye contact. Breathe with her and use touch relaxation. Be firm but gentle, and tell her exactly what she needs to do to make it through these difficult contractions. Keep the transition phase in perspective, knowing that it will not last forever. Don't panic. If you're feeling alone, ask for help from your support team (i.e., the nurse, doctor, your friends, or family) It is a very challenging time right before the baby is born, but you can do this! Be strong for her!

### Pant-Blow Transition Breathing

Blowing prevents additional pressure on the uterus by preventing the diaphragm (your breathing muscle) from moving downward. Equal exchanges of air (i.e., 3 seconds of air in and 3 seconds of air out), are recommended. The coach will say "contraction begins," then you take in your cleansing breath and make your "she, she" or "he, he" sounds using four sounds to one blow. Puff your cheeks while blowing. As you do this, use the coach's eyes as a focal point. Then the coach will then say "contraction's over." You will take another cleansing breath and relax.

### YOU

Practice your pant-blow breathing at home. Usually effleurage is not welcome during this stage of labor as the woman often does not want to be touched. Vary your practice sessions so that your practice contractions last between 60-90 seconds or longer. Your coach will count off the intervals to support you through the contractions. To simulate urgency and help you resist the urge to push, your coach will tap you on the shoulder.

### COACH

During this transition phase, your job is to call off 30 seconds intervals during each contraction, letting her know when it is "30-seconds," 60-seconds," and then "90-seconds. Because the contractions are longer during transition, the intervals are increased from 15-seconds to 30-seconds. You can use a stopwatch or a watch with a second hand to time the contractions. To allow her to practice breathing through the urge to push you can tap her on the shoulder to simulate urgency, when this happens she should then just do straight blowing to reduce her urge to push.

### FOR EXAMPLE

When your partner is doing "she, she" or "he, he" breathing, gently tap her on the shoulder to let her know it is time to blow. Vary when the urge to push will occur because it will not occur at regular intervals during her labor. Experiment with variations at home by holding up your fingers in a tapping motion or tapping on her shoulder to simulate the urge to push and let her know she needs to blow through that urgency. She can decide which works best for her, tapping on her shoulder or tapping in the air.

# STAGE 2 – DESCENT AND BIRTH OF THE BABY

- Begins when the woman is completely dilated to 10 centimeters.
- Contractions are one to three minutes apart.
- Contractions are strong in intensity and last 60-90 seconds with an urge to push.
- Ends with the birth of the baby.
- The average length of this stage is 30-120 minutes, but can be shorter or longer in duration.

### YOU

You may be feeling excitement, relief, and a sense of accomplishment. You may also forget how to push.

Women often get a second wind when they're told that they're 10 centimeters and it's time to push. Be aware that pushing too early causes the cervix to swell which can cause labor to slow down. Practicing pushing effectively can help you to hasten the birth of the baby during labor. Effective pushing increases the intra-thoracic and arterial pressure. For example: Picture an upside-down toothpaste tube being squeezed from the top with the toothpaste shooting out from the bottom. The use of force of the diaphragm muscle can exert pressure on the uterus, so it's important not to talk, groan, or breathe out when pushing.

**NOTE:** When you practice pushing, don't really push, because you don't want to initiate any premature rupture of membranes during your practice sessions.

Your main focus during this stage is to work with every single contraction and use the entire contraction when pushing. Follow your coach's direction. If you're instructed to stop pushing, lie back and do straight blowing to control the urge to push. If instructed to "hold the baby there," maintain your position and blow and control the urge to push. If instructed to give a half-push, blow out your air and fill your lungs partially and push with just half the effort.

## COACH

Encourage your partner to relax completely in between the contractions. Your role is to assist your partner into a pushing position and remind her how to push, giving the commands of an "inhale, exhale, inhale, exhale, inhale, swallow, position, focus, push, count to ten, exhale, cleansing breath." Remind her to relax her pelvic floor. Repeat the commands of the doctor or the nurse between contractions. Sponge her face, offer ice chips, adjust the pillows, and watch the birth.

When you are pushing, the nurse or doctor will need to see some of the baby's head (about the size of a two inch circle) before you are actually ready to be set up for the delivery. First time parents are often not prepared to see the infant's scalp when the head is still in the birth canal, right before the delivery. The vaginal opening enlarges as the baby moves down through the birth canal. Then the perineum begins to bulge and the crown of the baby's head appears. This is said to be the "crowning" of the baby's head when you can see at least a two-inch circle of the baby's head.

Right before the birth, your perineal area, the area from the vagina to the anus, will be cleansed with antiseptic scrub and warm water. Often you will be in just a birthing room where the bed will be adjusted for the delivery. A mirror can be positioned if you want to see the baby's birth. Each hospital has different policies regarding how many people are allowed in the birthing room. Usually it is good to keep the number of people at a minimum. You do not want your room to become too crowded and there may be some privacy issues, as well. The birth experience is a very personal one. Lately, it has become popular to have many people in the birthing room. I would think about it carefully, because too much commotion may detract from the very personal emotional experience between you and your partner. Your hospital and doctor will advise you as to their policies.

## POSITIONS FOR PUSHING

There are a number of different positions that you can be in when you are pushing. The position you choose should be most comfortable for you. However, your doctor may specify a position that will be best for your particular delivery. You should be confident in your choice and be able to coordinate muscle groups when pushing. The following are pushing options:

### Semi-reclining

The most popular birthing position is a semi-reclining pushing position. This position provides a good view for the nurse or doctor, shortens the labor time by 35%, and increases the pull of gravity.

### Side-lying or lateral

The side-lying or lateral position takes the pressure off your back. In this position, the perineum stretches slower, and there is a decreased need for an episiotomy. In the lateral position there is increased control during delivery, increased circulation to the baby, and allows for good eye contact between you and your coach. Also, in this position there is a decrease in the pull of gravity which may lengthen the time you are in labor.

### Knee-chest

In the knee-chest position you will be able to push on all fours—this takes the pressure off of your back and allows you to do pelvic rocking. The nurse or doctor may request this position if the baby's heart rate decreases. This is also the position of choice during fetal distress from a prolapsed cord. However, if you are in this position too long, it can cause weakness or numbness in your wrists. Note: this position cannot be used if you have an epidural.

### Squatting

Squatting is a fairly uncommon birthing position in our culture. This position increases the bearing-down efforts, increases the pelvic diameters, and is recommended for women with a small pelvis. This position increases the pull of gravity. The problem with this position is that it is a difficult position for the doctor or midwife delivering the baby. Note: this position cannot be used if you have an epidural.

### Standing

Standing increases the pelvic inlet or access, causes less pressure on the great vessels leading to and from the heart, increases the pull of gravity, and can shorten your time in labor. You can do pelvic tilting to relieve backache and increase the circulation to the baby. Some doctors and hospitals require that patients remain in bed during labor. Note: this position cannot be used if you have an epidural.

## Back

Lithotomy or back position provides a good view for the nurse, doctor or midwife, but this causes more back pain and poor circulation to you and your baby. You also may feel dizzy or nauseated with a headache and then the contractions are not as strong. This position decreases the pull of gravity and is not generally used except in certain medically indicated situations.

# WHAT IS AN EPISIOTOMY?

An episiotomy is an incision of the perineum (pelvic outlet) performed at the end of the second stage of labor. This is done to avoid laceration of the perineum and to facilitate delivery.

An episiotomy is especially recommended for large babies, when the baby is in a difficult position, with forceps deliveries, vacuum deliveries and emergency deliveries. This issue is an important one to discuss with your doctor ahead of time. At delivery, the doctor will make the ultimate decision.

A local anesthetic is infused into the tissue surrounding the perineum for pain reduction. In addition to the local anesthetic, the pressure of the baby's head on the perineum blocks the nerve endings and achieves a local anesthetic effect. You may experience a pulling sensation while the episiotomy is being done. Controlled relaxation and slow chest breathing may help to reduce the temporary discomfort. The episiotomy may be midline (in the center) or medial lateral (just to the side of center), depending on the size of the baby and the natural stretch of the perineum. After the delivery, the episiotomy is sutured with absorbable stitches.

There are pros and cons to having an episiotomy. On the pro side, a cut is easier to repair than a tear; it shortens the second stage of labor; and the delivery is more controlled. Take into account that an episiotomy will not prevent bladder weakness, restore pelvic floor muscles or guarantee that some tearing won't happen. On the con side, the recovery can be more uncomfortable.

Since the vaginal area is designed for childbirth, like a folded fan that enlarges for the delivery and then tightly folds into place afterwards, an episiotomy may not be necessary. Many feel that under normal conditions, with an average-sized baby and an average-sized pelvic outlet, simply massaging the perineum decreases the need for an episiotomy. In this case, the woman retains more control of the delivery.

Doing your Kegel exercises right away after delivery will aid in the healing process post delivery, and tone your perineal muscles. Kegel exercises also encourage blood flow to the vaginal area.

## OPTIONS FOR ASSISTED DELIVERY

The following are safe options the doctor may use to assist him or her in getting the baby delivered.

**Vacuum extractor** – Sometimes you just need a little bit of a boost at the end to deliver the baby's head. The vacuum extractor uses suction to help the head out. The doctor will apply a small cap to the baby's head and apply traction while you push in order to increase your pushing force. And again, usually local or regional anesthesia is used.

**Forceps** – Forceps are not used as commonly as they were in the past. Obstetrical forceps are used to assist in the delivery of the head or to rotate the baby's head to a more favorable position. They look like a "shoe horn" or "salad tongs" to help ease the baby's head out of a tight situation. Forceps may also be used if you are exhausted and unable to push effectively. Local or regional anesthesia is administered when forceps are used, but you should lie still and use controlled breathing when the forceps are applied.

# STAGE 3 — EXPULSION OF THE PLACENTA

People often forget that the Expulsion of the Placenta is a stage of labor. After the baby is born, the placenta comes out. The following will give you an idea of what to expect.

The placenta is expelled anywhere from 2 to 30 minutes after the birth, at which point you may notice a slight contraction. Usually, the placenta will be expelled spontaneously without much effort. Sometimes the doctor may need to assist in the delivery of the placenta.

---

### YOU

At this point you may be feeling excited, thinking of the baby, you may want to be alone with your husband and the baby, you may be tired and hungry, or you may have chills or be trembling. Your role is to push if directed to do so by your doctor; and if a vaginal exam is done you need to lie still and remain relaxed, using slow chest breathing or straight blowing. The vaginal exam is very important to make sure that the placenta has been completely expelled in order to avoid hemorrhage.

### COACH

Your role is to direct your partner when to push to deliver the placenta, assist with positioning, and help your partner relax when the vaginal exam is done. The doctor and nurse will be advising and helping you during this final stage of delivery.

---

*You may want to check with your doctor about preserving your baby's cord blood. The cord blood has an abundant source of stem cells. For more information, contact:*
www.americanpregnancy.org.

# CHAPTER SIXTEEN

# Delivery by Cesarean Section

## "The means of delivery is not as important as the outcome."

## THE ALTERNATIVE EXIT

Birth by a cesarean section or c-section (abdominal delivery), is an alternative mode of delivery and it is not a major catastrophe. If the baby is not able to be delivered vaginally, the doctor creates a "new door." A c-section is a safe, alternative way of delivering. Keep an open mind as you go into the delivery experience, knowing that a cesarean birth could be a possibility. With my third child, I pushed for three hours and then the decision was made to have a cesarean section. It turns out that my son was 10lbs 10oz! At any point a c-section may be called, even if this is not originally planned. Keep the mode of delivery in perspective. I was grateful to deliver my son by any means.

According to the 2004 national statistics, 29.1% of births are delivered by cesarean section. This statistic varies by hospital, city and state. Although there are situations where you may know ahead of time that you will have a c-section, usually the decision to deliver by c-section occurs once you are in labor. Possible reasons for a c-section include: prolonged labor, lack of progress, failed induction, breech, transverse or posterior position of the baby, twins/multiple births, prematurity, high blood pressure, heart disease, diabetes, placenta previa (where the placenta is presenting first before the baby), abruptio placenta (where the placenta detaches from the uterine wall), herpes virus or a previous c-section.

If you do have a c-section, the following may occur: You will sign a consent form and have blood work done. The hair above the mons pubis will be shaved. You will have an IV in your arm and a foley catheter will be inserted into your urethra in order to collect urine. Although these procedures may be uncomfortable, they are not painful. You'll have cardiac electrodes on your chest, possibly an oxygen mask as well, you will be given either a spinal, epidural (most common) or general anesthesia.

There are two main types of incisions used for a cesarean section. The most common one is called the "bikini cut" or Pfannenstiel incision (a horizontal incision). This incision is done at the pubic hair line. A vertical (up and down) incision is rare, and is done primarily if there is a very large baby or an emergency situation.

Once you have been moved to the operating room, sterile drapes will be placed over you so you will not actually see the surgery. Numerous personnel will be with you in the operating room. Your doctor will be the primary surgeon along with the assisting surgeon and the anesthesiologist. There will also be the scrub nurse, the circulating nurse and the nursery nurse. Generally, your coach and perhaps one other special person will remain with you during the delivery. Your coach will be seated beside you, at the head of the bed next to the anesthesiologist. The pediatrician is usually present at a c-section. It takes only about five minutes to deliver the baby and about 45 minutes to complete the suturing. Then you will be transferred to the recovery room for about an hour or so.

You will probably be very exhausted at this point, and very anxious to hold your baby. You will generally get to see and hold your baby in the operating room and the recovery room, depending on how you and your baby are doing. Immediately after your delivery, your vital signs will be monitored every 15 minutes and the fundus (the top of the uterus) will be massaged by the nurse. You will be carefully monitored in the recovery room by the recovery room nurse and staff.

Usually you will be out of bed and walking after 12-24 hours. Due to the increased blood supply to the uterus, healing after a c-section is more rapid than any other abdominal surgery. It is important to get up and walk after the first 12-24 hours to help avoid muscle stiffness, prevent blood clots and improve your ability to pass intestinal gas. The IV and the foley catheter are generally discontinued after 24 hours. It is also important to cough, breathe deeply, and change your position in bed every couple of hours. The nurse will assist you during this time. You may need extra assistance with positioning while breast-feeding your baby. The usual diet after a c-section is clear liquids until the bowel sounds are heard via a stethoscope and then it will be advanced to a regular diet. Sometimes the doctors will order antibiotics to prevent post-operative infections. You should expect to stay longer in the hospital – about three to four days and have a longer postpartum recovery. Your recovery will take longer, about eight weeks or so, because you delivered your baby and had major surgery. You will be encouraged to use pain medication and ask for extra help, should you need it.

Some women may feel like a failure if they don't deliver vaginally and some partners may feel "cheated" out of the birth experience. Acknowledge that you have been very successful in birthing your child, even if you had a c-section. The means of delivery is not as important as the outcome. How fortunate you are to live in a day and age where having a c-section is a very safe, alternate mode of delivery.

It's important not to have too many fantasies about the perfect birthing experience, and to be realistic going into labor, knowing it could be a vaginal or a cesarean delivery.

It is possible to have a vaginal birth after you've had a c-section. This is called a VBAC, a vaginal birth after cesarean. Whether you have a vaginal birth after a c-section will depend on the reason for the c-section, the type of incision you have on your uterus, and other variables. Your doctor can advise you about your options. Note: Generally the "bikini cut," or horizontal incision, is the most common type of incision. This is often done for cosmetic reasons. However what you see externally on you skin may not correspond to the incision made on your uterus. You should check with your doctor to find out what type of incision was made on your uterus. Sometimes a vertical incision is done on the uterus if the baby is large or in a difficult position. The type of incision made on your uterus will in part determine if you are a candidate for a VBAC in the future.

# CHAPTER SEVENTEEN

# Appearance of the Newborn

*"A baby enters the world with hands clenched, as if to say the world is mine and I shall grab it."*
—MIDRASH

## YOUR BABY'S APGAR SCORE

Your baby will be evaluated one minute after your baby is born and again at five minutes. Your baby's health status will be evaluated using the Apgar Score. The Apgar Score was developed by Dr. Virginia Apgar to assess a baby's physical health. The Apgar Score will evaluate the baby's heart rate (pulse), breathing (rate and effort), activity and muscle tone, grimace response ("reflex irritability") and appearance (color). Check with your doctor for more details regarding the Apgar Score.

## WHAT WILL YOUR NEW BABY LOOK LIKE?

Before you were pregnant you have probably thought about what your baby will look like, envisioning the perfect Hollywood picture of a newborn. It can be a surprise when you first gaze at your little bundle of joy for the first time and your baby looks nothing like you may have imagined. Your newborn will likely be screaming, wet and red, with a misshaped head.

There are variations in what is considered the normal, healthy appearance of a newborn baby. Many of the differences may be temporary. The following is a brief description of some of the newborn characteristics:

- **Color** – Immediately after birth, the baby's color is generally dark red to purple. As the baby takes its first breaths and becomes oxygenated, the color will become more pink. Sometimes the baby's face and body are pink but the extremities may be mildly bluish due to the baby's immature circulation.

- **Milia** – Tiny white pimples on the baby's nose, forehead and chin.

- **Lanugo** – soft hair on a newborn's cheeks, forehead, shoulders and back. Lanugo is more noticeable with premature babies

- **Vernix** – A cream cheese-like protective coating on the baby's body that will be absorbed into the skin and should not be scrubbed off. Babies that are born after 41 weeks often have dry flaky skin instead of vernix.

- **Molding (also spelled moulding)** – A "cone head," the slight misshaped head at birth due to the overlapping of the soft bones (fontanels) of the baby's head which allows it to pass through the birth canal.

- **Newborn breast swelling** – On the second or third day after birth, some babies, boys and girls, may develop slight breast swelling and secretion of milk from the nipples caused by the mother's hormones. This will soon go away.

- **Swollen genitals and discharge** – A newborn's genitals may be enlarged at birth. Some female newborns may also have a whitish and/or a slightly bloody mucous discharge coming from the vagina.

- **Mongolian spots** – Blue or purple-colored pigmented areas of the skin found on the baby's lower back and buttocks which are caused by a concentration of pigment in the skin. These spots usually fade by age four.

- **Stork bites** – Small pink or red patches found around the eyes, lips and back of the neck where the "stork picked up the baby." These generally fade completely in time.

# CHAPTER EIGHTEEN

# Stage Four—Postpartum: From Birth to Six Weeks

*"Honor your wife that you may be enriched."*

—*TALMUD*

## WHAT HAPPENS RIGHT AFTER DELIVERY

The Postpartum Stage begins when the baby is born and ends six weeks later. This stage can be referred to as the "oys and joys" of childbirth.

Directly after giving birth, you will be wrapped in a pre-warmed blanket (this feels like heaven!) and peri pads will be applied to the perineal area. You will probably remain in the room where you delivered, since most hospitals have Labor Delivery and Recovery (LDR) suites. Enjoy this time after your delivery to bond together as a family. You will generally have the opportunity to hold your baby (skin-to-skin contact) to bond with your baby and to try breastfeeding. Usually, you will stay in this room for two to four hours after the birth, although in some hospitals you will remain there until you are ready to go home.

You may experience some discomforts immediately after the baby is born. You may have uncontrollable chilling or shaking. You might not feel cold, but your body is shaking. This is due to the hormonal shifts that occur immediately after birth. Sometimes it can be relieved with a nice warm blanket or drinking some fluids or just by doing some slow relaxation breathing. You may be extremely thirsty and exhausted. You may experience the afterbirth cramps, which are postpartum contractions in the uterine area where the uterus goes from the size of a watermelon that took nine months to grow to the size of your fist. This process of involution takes about six weeks. The intensity of these cramps will lessen day by day. If you had a laceration or episiotomy, the area may be sore and swollen too. Usually an ice pack is applied to the perineal area. While you recover for the first hour, your blood pressure and pulse respiratory rate will be assessed every 15 minutes. The nurse will also be checking the amount of vaginal flow called lochia. This is actually a shedding of the lining of the uterus where the placenta detaches from the uterine wall. The detachment sight leaves a real wound that needs time to heal. This is not a regular menstrual period. You should only be using pads during this time, no tampons.

# A DESCRIPTION OF LOCHIA

### Lochia Rubra
Light to heavy flow, bright red bleeding and lasts 24-48 hours. Sometimes you might even pass some small or medium blood clots.

### Lochia Serosa
Small to moderate lochia which is serous (thin watery discharge) with pink streaks of blood. This lasts two days to two weeks.

### Lochia Alba
Scant brownish vaginal discharge that lasts two to six weeks.

By the third week, the vaginal flow, the lochia, will become scant and light and more brownish. At this stage, if you notice fresh bright red blood in large amounts you should call your doctor. It may be a sign that you're on your feet too much. The lochia should continue to decrease, not lessen and then increase. The amount and color of the lochia is the best index on how well the woman is healing inside.

A note about your menstrual periods: Usually your menstrual periods will return in six to eight weeks for non-nursing mothers and eight to ten months for nursing mothers, although for mothers who are exclusively breastfeeding, menstrual periods will often not return until after weaning. Remember, you **can** still get pregnant even if you are breast-feeding and have no periods!

The nurse will also massage the top of the uterus called the fundus to make sure it is nice and firm. This might be slightly uncomfortable and you can do some slow chest breathing during this time. The nurse will instruct you how to do the fundal massage by yourself. Your IV will be removed when the bleeding is controlled and vital signs are stable. During this time you will have something to eat and drink and then be assisted to the bathroom. It's a good idea to let the nurse help you up to the bathroom for at least the first three times until you are more steady on your feet.

During your hospital stay, it is important to do your Kegel exercises. Wonderful news: You can sleep on your stomach! You can request pain medication if it is needed, and usually what's ordered is Motrin, Advil, or Tylenol with Codeine. Drink plenty of fluids and eat a well-balanced diet including bran, fruits, vegetables, and protein. This is not a time for weight reduction. It is important to drink plenty of fluids to avoid developing urinary tract infections. Eating bran, fruits, and vegetables will help you have a bowel movement usually one to two days after you deliver.

It is important while you are recuperating to slowly start moving around. You do not want to stay in bed constantly, but again you also do not want to be on your feet too much. No jogging, of course.

The nurse will instruct you how to care for your episiotomy or laceration. You may be directed to use a special spray, witch hazel soaks, and/or a water bottle every time you go to the bathroom to rinse the perineal area. Each hospital has a protocol for this. Be cautious to wipe from front to back so you don't bring any fecal bacteria from the stool to the vaginal area.

Usually you can get up and shower 6-12 hours after delivery if you don't have any heavy bleeding, dizziness, or other problems. If you should develop hemorrhoids, which is swelling of the veins in the rectal area (they are just like varicose veins in the legs), the doctor may prescribe witch hazel soaks and in some cases a portable sitz bath where you sit in warm water few times a day. Hemorrhoids or an extensive episiotomy can be very uncomfortable and you may choose to lay on your side. Some doctors may prescribe an inflated inner tube upon which to sit.

During the first two days after delivery, the uterus is still the same size as right after the delivery, so make sure you bring loose fitting clothing to go home in, not tight jeans and a sweater, because your body will require time to get back to normal. Most women will still look about five-months pregnant at the time they are discharged from the hospital. The period of involution is the period of time in which the uterus decreases in size from that of a watermelon to the size of a fist, takes about six weeks. It is important once you are home to rest, to maintain good posture, do your Kegel exercises, and eat nutritiously. Realistic expectations will help you feel better about yourself during this postpartum stage.

The length of time that you recuperate in the hospital depends on how you are feeling, the hospital's policies, the doctor's orders and your medical insurance. Usually, for a normal vaginal delivery, you will stay one to two days after delivery, and for a cesarean section you will recuperate in the hospital for about three to four days.

## RUBIN'S PHASES

After giving birth, a woman may experience psychological changes, universally known as Rubin's Phases.

The first phase is called "Taking In." This phase usually happens during the first five days after delivery. During this time, you are very passive and dependent. You initiate little and wait for the actions of others. You tire easily with decision-making and physical activity. Sleep and food are most important for you after the baby is born. You relive and integrate the delivery experience. You are very talkative with family and friends who come to see you.

In the second phase, called "Taking Hold," you are concerned with striving for independence and autonomy. You are concerned about bodily functions, bowel and bladder performance, and, if you are nursing, you will be concerned about milk production. You can easily get upset over perceived "failures," such as the inability to burp the baby or to get him or her to eat. This is a normal reaction. Ask for help. Feeling and acting like a mother or father is generally a learned behavior, and not necessarily instinctive. Keep in mind that you may not instantly fall in love with your baby.

It is helpful to have your partner be the mediator between you and the outside world, and protect you from too many visitors and well-meaning relatives and friends. Their excitement may be a little overwhelming during this time. Learning about the Rubin's Phases will allow you and your partner to better understand your changing moods. Your partner's compassion and support will allow you to heal emotionally as well as physically.

# ONCE YOU'RE HOME

*"Little kids little problems,*
*big kids big problems."*
—MY GRANDMA

When you leave the hospital and go home with your baby, you may experience twinges of fear mixed with happiness and excitement. Keep in mind that there is a dramatic and emotional upheaval after the birth of a baby. This is a vulnerable time for both you and your partner as you transition from being a couple to becoming a family.

During your first week home with your new infant, life will be a bit easier if you protect yourself and your baby from the stress of too many visitors and small children. Too much chaos or attention can be overwhelming. Keeping a low profile can make your first week at home less stressful. One suggestion I have is to keep your life comfortable by wearing your "postpartum uniform," (your pajamas and a bathrobe) the first week or two at home. When you answer the door wearing your pajamas, people will understand that you are resting and will not stay too long. Attending to guests can become very exhausting.

It is advantageous to have help at home for the first week or two. It is a good idea to plan this in advance. Be cautious when choosing your helpers. If you know that someone is more likely to drive you crazy, they are not the best pick to help you with your new baby. Anytime you have someone in your home, tensions can arise. Choosing a friend or relative who blends well with your family will make life easier for all involved.

Helpers should do the housework and meal preparation, but you, the mom and the dad, are still the main caregivers for your baby. It is an important time for family bonding. It is OK to have relatives and friends cuddle and hold your new baby while making your first days at home an easier adjustment. You want to use this time to learn to care for your baby, while you have the support of your family and friends.

During the first week at home, focus on caring for yourself and your new baby's needs. During the second week, you may want to add one new activity each day and take baby steps to slowly add new activities.

Make sure you schedule your six-week postpartum checkup. Abstain from sexual relations until then to make sure everything has healed properly. You can still get pregnant before your first period, so you do want to have a birth control method on board. Use common sense about resuming sexual activity. A difficult labor or an extended episiotomy may take longer than six weeks to heal. It is usually safe to resume intercourse when the vaginal lochia is scant, brownish or non-existent, and you feel no perineal discomfort. In addition, intercourse may be painful since you are not yet ovulating and there may be a lack of vaginal moisture and secretions. You can use some water-soluble gel until you begin to menstruate again, at which time the vaginal lubrication returns. If you have a cesarean section, your doctor may want to see you for an incisional check-up one to two weeks after delivery. Check with your doctor on the specifics of your postpartum check-ups.

When you go for your postpartum visit, bring a list of questions for your doctor, including questions regarding resuming sexual relations with your partner and any other questions you might have. Any uncomfortable feelings, problems or concerns are encouraged to be discussed with your doctor.

### Advice for husbands

Consider planning an outside activity for you and your partner. About two weeks after the delivery, arrange for a babysitter you know well to care for your baby so you and your partner can enjoy a few moments alone— even if it's just for an hour, even if the new mom is breastfeeding. Have a date together! You can plan something as simple and easy as going to get ice cream or a quick bite to eat. Try to do this on a regular weekly basis. Whether your time away is for an hour walk or for an evening out, what's important is that you are spending time together as a couple. Making special time together a priority can help protect the intimate connection that brought you together in the first place. In addition, studies have shown that reserving this time together elevates your relationship, promotes bonding and reduces postpartum stress.

# RELAX...

*"what soap is for the body, tears are for the soul."*
—JEWISH PROVERB

As a couple, be very patient with each other. Do your Kegels religiously to enhance perineal muscle tone. Contract the perineal muscles as if you're trying to stop the flow of urine and then relax your muscles. You can also contract your perineal muscles while you're having sexual intercourse—contract your vaginal muscles around your husband's penis and then relax. As a reminder, review the section about Kegel exercises. If you are experiencing significant discomfort during intercourse more than six weeks postpartum, speak with your doctor.

The postpartum phase is a time of emotional, physical and hormonal highs and lows. Your husband may be worried about the change in household finances or jealous of the amount of time you have to spend with the baby. You may undergo hormonal changes. You will find less time for yourself and your husband. Spontaneity can be challenged. Before spending intimate time with your husband, it is a good idea to settle the baby first, making sure the baby is fed and diapered, etc. This gives you a better chance at fewer interruptions. Consider sleeping during the day whenever the baby is sleeping since nights can get very hectic.

A word about postpartum depression that may go beyond "baby blues." Do not be embarrassed to call your gynecologist even if you have no history of anxiety or depression before or during your pregnancy. If you do have a history of anxiety or depression, talk to your doctor *during* your pregnancy. Postpartum depression can happen to anyone and it should not be minimized. Some women may require medication for depression. This is a critical topic that needs attention and should be discussed with your health care provider. It is difficult for any individual to know when they have moved beyond "baby blues" and into the realm of depression. Ongoing communication with your doctor, partner and family members will allow others to support you in making the best choices during this challenging time.

# CHAPTER NINETEEN

# The Newborn Baby

*"Keep in mind that jaundice is common and generally a temporary situation."*

## JAUNDICE

The purpose of discussing newborn-baby jaundice is to make new parents aware of the possibility of jaundice since it occurs fairly frequently and is generally harmless. Jaundice, from the French word meaning yellow, is a yellow discoloration of the skin and eyes due to an accumulation of the bio-pigments in the blood known as bilirubin. Noticeable jaundice is found in about half of full-term babies or three-fourths of premature babies. Newborn-baby jaundice will generally resolve on its own without treatment.

Newborn-baby jaundice is not the same as jaundice that occurs in adults and is not the same having an adult alcoholic-fatty liver or liver disease. In an adult, this disease is caused by the malfunction or obstruction of the liver or intestines.

The most common type of newborn-baby jaundice is physiologic jaundice. Physiologic jaundice is only found in newborns and occurs when the enzymes in the newborn perform the normal process of breaking down red blood cells creating an increase in bilirubin. At the same time, the baby's liver is still immature and not functioning at full capacity during the baby's first few weeks. This type of jaundice is very temporary and will generally subside in one to two weeks. Another type of jaundice is an RH or ABO Incompatibility Jaundice. This is when the hemolysis or premature destruction of the infant's red blood cells occurs due to the incompatibility between the mother's blood and the baby's blood. This is a more serious situation. It does not mean that anything permanent is happening to your newborn. However, in the process of resolution, within one to two weeks, it is important that the bilirubin levels be monitored to make sure they do not get too high. Dangerously high levels of bilirubin in the baby's blood is called kernicterus and is a condition that requires prompt medical intervention.

Some statistics show that one out of every 200 breast fed babies will develop physiologic jaundice. This will pass in one to two weeks. Breast milk itself is not harmful at all. There is a substance in some mother's milk that may temporarily inhibit enzyme activity in the liver. If this happens, there is a rise in the bilirubin level which can be seen in the second or third week. It is recommended that the mother continue breastfeeding during this time, since physiologic jaundice does pass on its own. Keeping your baby hydrated with breast milk or formula is very important.

The main treatment for newborn jaundice is phototherapy where the baby is exposed to light to assist in the breakdown of bilirubin, which is light-sensitive. It is vital that phototherapy not be undertaken without the direction of your physician. Consult with your baby's doctor regarding your baby's condition to determine the best medical treatment plan. Even though most babies with jaundice recover completely within a few days or weeks, the experience can be stressful and exhausting to new parents. Keep in mind that jaundice is common and generally a temporary situation. Babies may remain in the hospital during treatment or in some cases, when the jaundice is not as severe, phototherapy can be given at the home by a visiting nurse. Some doctors may advise using indirect sunlight as part of your baby's treatment.

# CHAPTER TWENTY

# Breastfeeding and Bottlefeeding

*"Tap into your own inner resources, harness your energy, and above all: stay calm."*

## BREASTFEEDING

*"How will I feed my baby?"*
*"Can every woman breast feed?"*
*"Can I do both breast and bottle feeding?"*

This is a very personal choice that ultimately is yours to make on your own. It is helpful to take into account many factors before making your choice. Educating yourself and your partner about breastfeeding while you are pregnant is a helpful and proactive plan that will serve you well. Sometimes a lack of preparation and knowledge alone can cause some women to be unsuccessful at breastfeeding. Most couples are very focused on the delivery day, and its difficult to even picture yourself as a breastfeeding mommy!

There are many ways to get information on breast-feeding. You can read a breastfeeding book, connect with friends and /or relatives who have breast fed, contact your local breastfeeding organizations, confer with your doctor and/or enroll in a lactation course often available at your local hospital. In order to create a realistic expectation on breastfeeding, advance preparation is the key. It is a good idea to prepare your nipples for breastfeeding during pregnancy. One way is by nipple rolling. You can gently pull out the nipple with your thumb and index finger and carefully roll it back and forth. This can be done once a day. Also you can use a dry washcloth to rub over the nipples to help toughen them. It is also good to go braless a few times during the day to help toughen the nipples. Don't worry if you decide to breastfeed at the last minute. If you didn't prepare your nipples during pregnancy, you can still breastfeed successfully. Knowledge is your ticket to your lactation success! Any amount of time that you are able to spend breastfeeding is good for your baby. New moms often have a tendency to feel stressed when it comes to the topic of breastfeeding. Relax and enjoy the journey during this very special time.

*The following is a brief overview about breastfeeding and not meant to replace any breastfeeding book, course, or doctor's advice.*

There are many advantages of breastfeeding for both mother and baby. Breast milk generally provides ideal nourishment for your baby. Human milk for human babies is the perfect combination! Breast milk helps boost your baby's immune system. Breastfeeding promotes bonding between you and your baby. Breastfeeding also develops the face and jaw muscles of the newborn, saves money and time and breast milk is always ready at the optimal temperature. Breastfeeding can also help the new mom recover after delivery. When the baby suckles, special hormones are released, causing your uterus to contract returning it to a smaller size. When you breastfeed, the hormone prolactin is secreted, which gives you a feeling of calmness, well-being, and serenity. There's nothing quite like this experience. I felt so peaceful when I breastfed that I could sit on my rocking chair all day long and breastfeed my baby and feel so content. This is a wonderful, special time. In my opinion, it is one of the highlights of having children. Long-term benefits of breastfeeding include decreasing your risk of developing breast and ovarian cancer.

After the birth of your baby, you will experience the "let-down reflex," which is a tingling sensation as milk is filling up in your breasts. This is caused by the mammary cells that line the breast tissue, propelling the milk fluid toward the ducts behind the areola. This is described as when your milk is "coming in and letting down." My "let down reflex" was so sensitive that if I heard a puppy whimper or a kitten meow I would suddenly be wet with tons of milk!

Two important facts you must be aware of when it comes to breastfeeding:
- Mothers who drink excessive amounts of alcohol while nursing risk losing optimal milk production. In addition, alcohol passes into your breast milk directly to your baby.
- Heavy cigarette smoking while nursing may cause a decrease in your milk production. (Exposure to second-hand smoke can have an impact on the baby as well).

You should not be using alcohol or cigarettes at all when you are breastfeeding. All drugs are present in your breast milk, and some drugs may be harmful to your baby. Always check with your doctor regarding any prescription medication you may be taking.

Be aware that some babies do not nurse well right after delivery. Gentle persistence, patience, and a sense of humor are your recipe for success! Ask a lot of questions and be receptive to any positive advice and support. Get as comfortable as you can when you are breastfeeding. Hold your baby using pillow support and experiment with different nursing positions. Newborns have what is called a "rooting reflex." When you gently brush your nipple on the baby's cheek, the baby will "root," that is, go in the direction of and latch onto your breast. You will learn from your baby's cues when he or she wants to nurse. Each time you nurse, you will become more comfortable with breastfeeding.

Proper latch-on techniques will help prevent your nipples from becoming sore. The use of lanolin cream and air drying your nipples are both very helpful techniques. Although, you should refrain from using lanolin if you have an allergy to wool. You'll want to air dry your nipples five to ten minutes after each feeding by putting down the flaps on your nursing bra. In addition, drink plenty of fluids and use a supportive bra.

Remember to start feeding your baby on a different breast each time so that your breasts will produce equal amounts of milk and you won't end up lopsided!

When you breast-feed, you will experience some very sharp cramps at the start of every nursing session for the first few days. These cramps occur as your uterus contracts and is nature's way of returning your body to its pre-pregnant state. When you begin nursing, the "first milk" is called the colostrum and is very nutritious for your baby. Colostrum is a valuable first food that provides protein, minerals, and antibodies. "True milk" comes in after about 48 hours.

The primary engorgement or the "coming in of your milk" within the first 48 hours after birth can scare some women off the idea of breastfeeding because it seems as if the heaviness of their breasts will last forever! This is a temporary situation and it only lasts about one week or less. It is important to prepare for this experience ahead of time, as much as possible. Your breasts may feel very tender, hot, and heavy. Taking a nice warm shower, wearing a supportive bra, and frequent nursing will help. It is important to be aware of the difference between primary engorgement and mastitis, a breast infection where the breast becomes red and hard, usually accompanied by a fever. If this occurs, you need to call your doctor right away. Your doctor will generally prescribe antibiotics and recommend placing cold packs on your breasts, such as frozen cabbage leaves.

Breast milk is produced based on supply and demand. The more the baby suckles, the more milk will be produced. So it is important to be relaxed and nurse your baby every two to three hours during the day. Drink lots of fluids. Be comfortable while breastfeeding, have adequate rest and good nourishment. In addition, nursing your baby every two to three hours during the day will help your baby sleep longer during the night.

In certain situations, you can use a breast pump which will allow you to give your baby your breast milk in a bottle. There are many combinations of breast and bottle feeding, and usage of the breast pump, so be sure to enlighten yourself on this interesting subject. You can discuss this topic with your doctor if you have any questions or concerns about introducing bottle feeding once you are breastfeeding.

Breastfeeding is a subject that is often overlooked until the task is at hand. I can't emphasize enough the importance of attending breastfeeding classes as well as reading a good book about breastfeeding. You will want to learn everything you can about this topic. For more information contact *www.breastfeeding.com* and *www.babycenter.com*.

# BOTTLEFEEDING

You can enjoy a wonderful, special bond with your baby whether breastfeeding or bottlefeeding or a combination of both. If you decide to bottle feed, do not feel guilty about making this choice. It is better to feel confident and relaxed while bottle feeding, rather than tense and nervous breastfeeding. There are circumstances in which babies need to be bottlefed. What is most important is the love you give your baby.

It is recommended to prepare ahead of time and learn as much as possible about the subject of bottle feeding. There are many types of bottles and formulas and you will want to do your own research.

Formulas supply ample nutrients and calories to allow babies to thrive. Your doctor can counsel you in the choice of which formula may be best suited for your baby. As I mentioned before, this is a very personal decision that must feel right for you and your baby.

Holding your baby during feedings is important. Babies thrive on the pleasure of being held during their feedings. Propping up a bottle during feedings is dangerous and could result in the baby choking. You want to be present at all times while your baby is feeding in order to monitor your baby's safety.

If you are bottle feeding your baby, be sure to carefully read the directions for mixing formula. Powders are less expensive than prepared cans of formula. Do not over or under-dilute the formula.

*Note*: Do not use honey with children under two years old, due to their immature immune system since honey can carry C. Botulinum spores which may be harmful to babies.

Family members can participate in the feedings too, and this embraces your baby in a warm circle of love. For more information contact: *www.babycenter.com* and *www.babyzone.com/baby/feeding/nutrition/bottle.*


# CHILDBIRTH EDUCATION SUMMARY

## "May You Grow From Strength to Strength."
### – JEWISH SAYING

### *Mazal Tov on completing the Childbirth Education section!*

You now have a firm knowledge base from which to draw upon for support. Be patient with yourself; it is not easy to absorb and process all of this new information. Tap into your own inner resources, harness your energy, and above all: stay calm. Put this knowledge to work during these exciting but challenging times.

As an explorer, you are traveling in a new territory with many unknowns. It is likely that you (and your partner) may feel lost at times. We hope that the L'Mazeltov section on Childbirth Education will help you stay on track.

You have so much to look forward to! Take hold of the strength, courage and spirit to be confident in labor and delivery. Many well-meaning family and friends will be offering you advice and feel that they are entitled to do so! They start to touch your growing belly and have an opinion about everything! Pregnancy is a real ice breaker and you will be the conversation piece whether you volunteer for this or not! You have the practical knowledge and wisdom to sift through these comments and accept or reject them as you see fit.

Keep your sense of humor . . . this is very crucial during these special days.

We wish you a quick labor and easy delivery. May you and your baby be blessed with good health, prosperity and many Mitzvot.

L'Mazeltov links two ideas together of Childbirth Education and Jewish Life Cycle Education. Now is the time to embark on the next leg of your exploration—the Jewish Life Cycle Education section. Remember, it is most important to enjoy the journey.

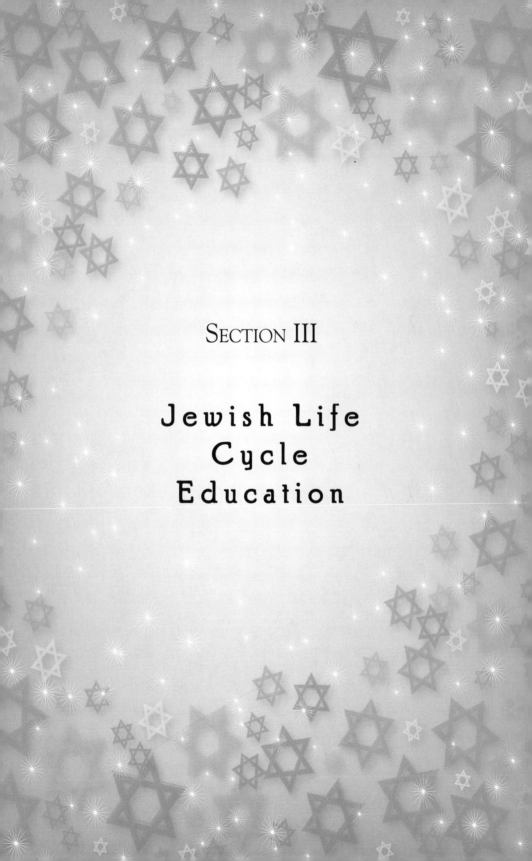

SECTION III

Jewish Life
Cycle
Education

"Train up a child the way he should go and when he is old he will not depart from it."

—PROVERBS

CHAPTER TWENTY-ONE

# An Introduction

*"To everything there is a season, and a time to every purpose under heaven."*
*—ECCLESIASTES 3:1*

## CREATING YOUR JEWISH LIFE TOGETHER

Judaism cherishes life! It is a joy to be part of a People that embraces such a rich Jewish heritage. The heart and soul of the Jewish People is in our very own homes. Our home is our nest, our holy square-footage in a physical sense, an emotional haven from the often chaotic and challenging world. Our home is our primary sanctuary, where we have security and safety for ourselves and our families.

Jewish tradition has always paid close attention to our deepest human feelings and needs. Judaism gives significance and relevance to our innermost emotions. Judaism elevates landmark life events such as birth through the use of ritual blessings and prayers. Jewish rituals create the pathways to appreciate and grow from our life's experiences. Living a life of significance—that is, a life that has meaning, a life that really matters—is by choice, not by chance. L'Mazeltov can help you create your own personal Jewish home for your precious new baby.

*"children are our hope and legacy
to the future of our people."*
—SHIR HASHIRIM RABA

L'Mazeltov is a natural beginning for Jewish expectant couples. It is the jump-start for beginning your Jewish family life together.

Your home will be the single most important influence in the Jewish upbringing and fundamental Jewish education of your precious gift from G-d, your newborn. Your home is the foundation of our religion and the core of being a Jewish person. Take the time and effort to spiritually and physically build a Jewish home that is a positive and responsive center in your child's life.

As your child's parents, it is your sacred privilege and responsibility to provide for his or her emotional, physical, and spiritual needs. Approach this honor with abundant joy and vigor! Begin your pregnancy to create your own Jewish home—the one that you have always wanted.

*"And you shall choose life, so that
you and your children may live."*
—DEUTERONOMY 30:19

## SPECIAL ADVICE TO HUSBANDS

Your wife's pregnancy is an occasion for you to shine, a golden opportunity to be a real *mensch* of a husband and human being. (The  Yiddish word *mensch* often refers to being a decent, caring, responsible, honorable person—an all-around great person.)

> *"A man must always be exceedingly*
> *careful to show honor to his wife."*
> —THE BABYLONIAN TALMUD, BABA MEZIA

Compassionate acts, gentleness and concern by a husband for his wife during pregnancy is essential and greatly appreciated. Some ways to show honor to your wife while she is pregnant include getting involved in the pregnancy and childbirth process by attending childbirth education classes. Participate by reading books about pregnancy, childbirth and parenting, attending doctors' appointments, taking infant CPR and lactation classes with your wife. Together take steps to integrate Jewish values, rituals, practices and traditions into your home.

Take time to listen to your wife with patience and compassion. Find out what she needs and wants from you while she is carrying your baby. Listen to her fears and concerns, and allow her to share her feelings with you without feeling that you need to "fix it" unless, of course, she is actually asking you to fix something.

> *"A man should love his wife as himself*
> *and honor her more than himself."*
> —BABYLONIAN TALMUD, YEVAMOT

Sometimes our behavior in a marriage or intimate relationships is not always as honoring or respectful as it might be in other relationships. Occasionally a man will say things about his wife in public that he would never say about his business partner if he intended to continue working with him or her. A husband is advised to afford the same or greater respect to his wife. In addition, we often fail to fully express our love and appreciation for our marriage partners (and to our family members, as well). "Oh, she knows I love her" is not enough. Verbally expressing our love and appreciation is vital to the success of the relationship. But, remember that "talk is cheap" and words are not enough. Supplement your loving words with actions that convey your love for your partner as well. Take time to check in with your wife to make sure she feels that you love her *as you love yourself*. Obviously, a wife is similarly obligated to love her husband as herself.

Emotional connection between couples can be shared in many different ways. I had witnessed a husband who experienced a compassionate and devoted connection with his wife. He spoke as if he were having contractions along with his wife during "their" pregnancy and labor. His words conveyed his connection to his wife's physical experience, as he told the doctor: "My wife's contractions are hurting us" and "we feel the baby move."

*"You have put gladness in my heart."*
—PSALMS 48

Allow your actions to show your wife how much you love and appreciate her and tell her how you feel about her, and how much you love her. You can begin to integrate different rituals designed to acknowledge each other in your relationship. Jewish tradition gives us some tools to express our appreciation. It is a nice tradition to sing Eshet Hayil (A Woman of Valor) to your wife on *Erev Shabbat* (Friday evening), as you bring in the Sabbath together. You have the power to create Sh'lom Bayit—peace in the home—by expressing that you love, cherish and appreciate your wife, during the pregnancy and childbirth experience, and throughout your life together.

*"The world is new to us every morning—this is G-d's gift; and every man should believe he is reborn each day."*
—BAAL SHEM TOV

*L'Mazeltov*

# IN THE BEGINNING

*"In the beginning . . . and G-d*
*saw that it was good."*
—GENESIS

Judaism is one of the oldest religions in the world; it is over 3,500 years old. Whether you are born Jewish or become Jewish by choice, you belong to a people that have given the world a deep spiritual, ethical, and cultural heritage. Judaism connects us with other Jews throughout the world. Judaism directs us in our relationships with ourselves, with each other and with G-d, with no intermediaries. Judaism calls for the best within us. It promotes positive development of character, fulfillment of our natural abilities, and the creative growth of our personalities. Judaism promotes awareness, compassion, responsibility and connection to the world around us.

*"You shall do what is proper and*
*good in the eyes of G-d."*
—DEUTERONOMY 6:18

L'Mazeltov offers you a springboard for bringing your child into this sacred and value-rich community, the covenant of the Jewish people. Some of the basic values of Judaism, in reference to raising a Jewish child, include:

- Regarding all life as sacred.
- Loving and revering G-d.
- Respecting human dignity.
- Striving for holiness.
- Caring for those who are ill.
- Having compassion for all creatures.
- Performing acts of lovingkindness.
- Not destroying needlessly.
- *Tzedakkah* – giving to or assisting those in need.
- *Tikkun Olam* – an obligation to improve our world.
- Seeking peace and being an instrument for peace.

> *"He who saves a single life,*
> *saves the entire world."*
> —TALMUD

In addition, Judaism encourages us to bring Jewish values, traditions and practices into our homes, to support the people of Israel, and to study Torah as a path to becoming better human beings.

## GETTING STARTED

> *"He who executes charity and justice is*
> *regarded as though he has filled the*
> *entire room with kindness."*
> —THE TALMUD

It's fun to get started in creating your Jewish home environment! You might begin by integrating holiday celebrations into your life or by adding Jewish books to your library. You might take classes, check out

Jewish music, recipes, toys, art, ritual objects and more. Enjoy being together as you discuss and discover how you want your Jewish home to feel.

The following are some suggestions for bringing Judaism into your home starting now, while you are pregnant:

- Affix a *Mezuzah* on your door—this is a sign of a Jewish home.
- Start having *Shabbat* dinners in your home. Invite family and friends over and start a new tradition. You can light the *Shabbat* candles, do the Kiddush, say the *Hamotzi* prayer and sing *Shabbat* songs. You can even bake a Challah! (see recipe section).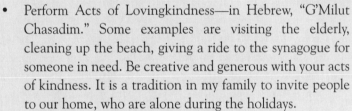
- Have a Tzedakkah box in your home. Every day, drop in some coins and say a blessing. When the box is full, give the money to the cause of your choice.
- Perform Acts of Lovingkindness—in Hebrew, "G'Milut Chasadim." Some examples are visiting the elderly, cleaning up the beach, giving a ride to the synagogue for someone in need. Be creative and generous with your acts of kindness. It is a tradition in my family to invite people to our home, who are alone during the holidays.
- Learn Hebrew – it is an important aspect of Judaism.
- Support Jewish museums, exhibits, restaurants, movies and theater. Enjoy Hebrew/Jewish music by listening and dancing. Attend Jewish concerts, buy Jewish CDs and books, attend a Jewish book fair. This can be a lot of fun and very rewarding.
- Check out the programs at your local Jewish Community Center.
- Find a local synagogue and start attending services. Join other couples at Jewish holidays and events. Find out

where there is a Purim party or Yom Hatzmaut (Israel Independence Day) celebration.

- Learn about your own family's Jewish heritage. Talk to family members about their life experiences and how they celebrate the holidays.
- Display Jewish ritual objects in your home. Let family members know how much you would appreciate these items as gifts. Such items include *Shabbat* candle holders, Menorah and a Kiddush cup.
- Say the "Shema" prayer before you go to sleep at night and when you wake up in the morning. This will increase your feelings of well being and peace.
- Try out new recipes in your kitchen. Cook and eat Jewish foods. Have a "new Jewish recipe" potluck with friends and family. Get some recipes from Grandma.
- Read Jewish books and tell Jewish stories. Add Jewish books to your collection.

A Midrash tells us that when G-d was ready to give the Torah to the People of Israel at Mount Sinai He asked, "What guarantee will you give me for my Torah?" The People of Israel answered, "The Patriarchs, Abraham, Isaac, and Jacob have their faults. The Prophets have their faults, too. Let our children be our guarantee." G-d responded, "They are the best guarantee. I will accept your children."

*"If I am not for myself, who will be for me? And if I am only for myself, what am I? And if not now, when?"*
—Rabbi Hillel

Pregnancy reminds me of the celebration of Passover, which is called the Seder. The word "Seder" means order, and there is an order to life's most awesome event, the birth of your child, G-d's most precious gift. During the early stages of your pregnancy, you begin to

*L'Mazeltov*

prepare on many levels: buying the layette and crib, moving to a larger home, changing work hours or painting the baby's room—these are just a few of the many changes that may happen and you will need to be prepared for.

There is also "Seder", a natural order of what occurs at each interval of your pregnancy. Lab tests are ordered at certain times, ultrasounds show characteristics of your baby at certain stages of development, when you "feel life" for the first time, what medications are safe or unsafe during which months of pregnancy, and what exercises should be done and when. All of this happens in a specific order and sequence during your pregnancy.

The trimesters of pregnancy also reflect this concept of "Seder", or order. There are three trimesters of pregnancy, and certain developmental milestones are met with each trimester. It is fascinating to observe how the baby physically grows and matures in a specific and orderly manner.

There is "Seder" to labor and delivery itself: how labor starts, each stage of labor and delivery, and the stages afterwards, including the Postpartum stage. There are specific physical as well as emotional characteristics of healing and recovery from the birth.

This idea of "Seder"—that is, getting ready in a Jewish tradition, gives sanctity to the many preparations. Your generation has really mastered the art of multi-tasking, doing more than one thing at a time. Combining Childbirth Education with the Jewish Life Cycle Education in L'Mazeltov is a very efficient solution for a busy couple! Appreciate all the changes in your body, and the "Seder" (order) to which it occurs . . . it is truly a miracle!

"To every purpose there is a season . . . a time to laugh, a time to cry . . . " is a beautiful quote from the Bible. This elaborates the thought of timing and the order of the universe. L'Mazeltov strives to give holiness to the routine, elevates the mundane, and uplifts your life in a very positive way. Isn't it a miracle that the baby's ears form and the baby's heart beats and all this happens in a set and orderly manner? What a wonderful time in your life to renew yourself, replenish yourself, and be a part of the creation of another!

This is the time to evaluate what's important to you, to explore and create your vision of your Jewish home. Pregnancy provides a unique opportunity to connect more deeply with your Jewish roots and to establish and fine-tune your Jewish patterns. It's a time to commit your hearts and souls to your new baby—the newest member of the next generation. This is your opportunity to create the kind of home that you have always wanted, an important piece of your child's Jewish inheritance.

> *"G-d is peace, G-d's name is peace, and all is bound together in peace."*
> —ZOHAR

Sh'lom Bayit, Hebrew for "Peace in the Home", is a beautiful Jewish concept that promotes a peaceful way of life in your home. Peace in our world begins in our homes. When you are expecting a baby, you are preparing yourself, your home, and your life on many levels.

The teachings of Judaism encourage you to be present, stay aware and appreciate the changes in your day, your life, your relationships, your body and in your heart and soul. Judaism gives holiness to the routine tasks.

L'Dor V'Dor—from generation to generation—refers to the passing of Jewish values, teachings and traditions from one generation to the next generation. This is your legacy and our future, and it begins now.

> *"Just as my ancestors planted for me, so shall I plant for my children."*
> —TA'NIT 32A

From the minute that you hear the great news that you are pregnant, changes in your life start to happen right away. You choose to eat healthier foods, get more sleep, and make changes in your lifestyle including spiritual changes. Becoming pregnant is the time for you to take a look at the type of atmosphere you choose to have in your home. Don't wait until your child is ready for Hebrew School! You are the architect of your child's Jewish future and the time to start planning is now- from the very beginning.

If you are making a change from secular to traditional Judaism, you may experience some resistance from your own circle of friends, co-workers, and even your own family. What may be popular or the norm in your community may tempt you to just fit in with everyone else. You may even cause a positive change within your family or group of friends.

Together, it's OK to be different! Have the courage to be the trendsetters, take a stand, and be admired and respected for the path you have chosen. The energizing Jewish lifestyle can be very contagious!

*"The lessons of youth are not easily forgotten."*
—TALMUD

L'Mazeltov discusses Jewish life cycle events, Jewish values, ethics, rituals and customs, with references to the Bible, Talmud, Midrash, and other Jewish literature.

*Judaism has three main Ceremonies of Life events:*

**For Birth**
Brit Milah/Bris (circumcision) for a boy.
Brit Chayim (baby naming ceremony) for a girl.

**For Puberty**
Bar and Bat Mitzvah.

**For Marriage**
The Chuppah and Kiddushin.

**Some of the topics include:**

- Special prayers for the time of birth.
- The sacred covenant between G-d and Abraham.
- *Brit Milah* or *Bris* (Circumcision) for the boy and *Brit Chayim* (Baby Naming ceremony) for the girl.
- *Pidyon Haben* (redemption of the first born male).
- The value of *Torah*, *Chuppah*, *Mitzvot*, and *Tzedakkah*.
- The traditional *Ashkenazi* and *Sephardic* customs in choosing a Hebrew name.
- Jewish folk customs surrounding the birth of the newborn.
- Your parental obligation according to the *Talmud*.
- The *Halachic* status of the adopted child.
- The beauty of *Shabbat* and the Jewish holidays.
- The blessing of the children.
- The significance of various blessings and prayers such as the *Shehecheyanu*, *Shema*, *Kiddush*, the blessing over the *Shabbat* candles, *Hamotzi*, and *Birkat Hamazon*.
- The vital importance of *L'dor V'dor* (from generation to generation), the Jewish tradition of strengthening the Jewish population.
- The special place of honor held by grandparents.
- The importance of having and displaying Jewish books and symbols in the home.

Blessings and prayers in Hebrew, English transliteration and English, are found throughout this text, including those for candle lighting, parents' blessing over the children, the *Kiddush*, the *Hamotzi* and more.

During the next nine months and beyond, use L'Mazeltov as a guide to help you explore, learn, discover and create this next important phase of your lives together.

# SPECIAL PRAYERS FOR TIME OF BIRTH

## A Psalm for Labor and Delivery

### SHIR LAMA'ALOT – SONG OF ASCENTS

This is a very meaningful psalm for the time of birth, according to Kabbalah. Shir Lama'alot offers protection for the laboring mother and the newborn child. It is traditional for laboring Jewish women to carry a card with this psalm throughout the labor and delivery. This psalm gives them comfort and peace, knowing that G-d is watching over them. Shir Lama'alot is a beautiful tradition that all women may wish to embrace.

After the child is born, it is customary to place this card on the baby's crib. Some also hang a card on the doorway of the baby's room. Shir Lama'alot is a quest for G-d's protection for both mother and child. This special psalm is a symbol that your baby's Jewish education starts at birth.

## A Song of Ascents (Psalm 121)

*I lift my eyes to the mountains – where will my help come from?*
*My help comes from the L-rd, Maker of heaven and earth.*
*He will not let your foot falter; your guardian will not slumber.*
*Indeed, the guardian of Israel will neither slumber nor sleep.*
*The L-rd is your guardian; the L-rd is your shade at your right hand.*
*The sun will not harm you by day, nor the moon at night.*
*The L-rd will guard you from all harm; he will watch over your soul.*
*The L-rd will guard your coming and going, now and forever.*

L'Mazeltov will be honored to send you a complimentary Shir Lama'alot card. Contact us at *WWW.LMAZELTOV.ORG*. We appreciate the opportunity to do this Mitzvah.

## Shehecheyanu Prayer

In Jewish tradition, when a child is born, the Shehecheyanu prayer is recited. It is a prayer of gratitude and thanksgiving. We are in awe of the creation of life, birth and the miracle of the new baby. Giving birth gives sanctity to G-d's abundant blessings and we are very appreciative to be present for such a life-changing event.

It is a Mitzvah to express one's gratitude through prayer and Tzedakkah for the safe and healthy birth of a child and the wellbeing of the child's mother.

## The Shehecheyanu Prayer

ברוך אתה ה׳ אל-הינו מלך העולם
שהחינו וקימנו והגיענו לזמן הזה

*BARUCH ATA ADO-NAI ELO-HEINU MELECH HA-OLAM,*
*SHEHECHEYANU VE'KIYEMANU VE'HIGI ANU LAZ'MAN HAZEH*

Blessed art thou, L-rd our G-d, Ruler of the universe,
who has kept us alive and sustained us
and allowed us to reach this moment.

Once your baby is born, you will want to call your Rabbi to make specific arrangements for the Baby Naming Ceremony for a girl and the *Brit Milah* (Circumcision) for a boy. It is a good idea to connect with your Rabbi prior to the actual birth, as well.

# CHAPTER TWENTY-TWO

# "Brit Milah"
# (Circumcision)

*"It is a Mitzvah to have a*
*Brit Milah on the eighth day."*

## CEREMONY FOR A BOY

*Brit* (the Sephardic pronunciation) or *Bris* (the Ashkenazi pronunciation) is the Hebrew word meaning covenant. The *Brit Milah* is the "Covenant of Circumcision." A *Brit Milah* is the religious ritual of circumcision in which Jewish male babies are formally welcomed into Judaism on the eighth day of their life. A circumcision is a surgical operation performed by a *Mohel*, an observant Jew who has been carefully trained to perform the circumcision. The baby boy is given his name at the *Brit Milah* Ceremony.

In Judaism, we believe that life is holy and birth is the most meaningful of all occasions.

There are many important components of the *Brit Milah*.
- The *Mohel*, the ritual circumciser, is a pious Jew who studies the surgical procedure of circumcision. Nowadays some Jewish pediatricians may also be trained as *Mohels*. *Mohels* are very professional and must pass strict government tests to earn a license. A qualified *Mohel* will make sure the

entire procedure is done according to the highest medical standards and that it is acceptable according to *Halacha* (Jewish law). Keep in mind that a *Mohel* has extensive medical training and experience, and will likely conduct many more circumcisions than a surgeon each year.

- The circumcision is done on the eighth day because this is considered to be the optimal time for the infant in a physical sense. The infant's nervous system has not fully matured so there will be less pain experienced by the baby. In addition, the baby's physical resources such as clotting are stronger and at their best by the eighth day.

- It is a *Mitzvah* to have a *Brit Milah* on the eighth day. The days are counted between the birth and the *Brit Milah* so if the child is born on a Monday before nightfall, the *Brit Milah* is on a Monday during the day. The Torah states that the *Brit Milah* ceremony is performed on the eighth day, and it is performed even if it should fall on *Shabbat* or *Yom Kippur*.

- It is important to note, that if for any reason the infant has a health problem on the eighth day, the *Brit Milah* should be delayed and only take place once the health problem or emergency is over. In keeping with Judaism's commitment to life, the safety and health of the child is always placed first.

- A *Brit Milah* is usually performed in your home, although it may be performed in the hospital or in a synagogue. You can have a Jewish or non-Jewish doctor oversee the *Mohel*, if you choose to do so. However, the *Mohel* performs the circumcision.

- Circumcision alone without the appropriate prayers does not constitute entrance into the covenant. It is considered a *Mitzvah* for every Jewish male child to be brought into the covenant and into the community with prayer and appropriate ritual.

- As part of the *Brit Milah*, it is customary to have a

reception with family and friends gathering in the home. It is customary but not mandatory that you have a Minyan (a quorum of ten Jews present) in order to have a *Brit Milah*.

- Making arrangements for the preparation of the *Brit Milah* is generally the responsibility of the father but it may be shared by both parents, family and friends.
- Your *Mohel* or Rabbi can assist you in making the arrangements for your *Brit Milah* ceremony and advise you on all the necessary components.

*"children are our hope and legacy to the future of our people."*
—SHIR HASHIRIM RABA

# THE SETUP AND DUTIES OF THE BRIT MILAH CEREMONY

The duties of the *Brit Milah* rest mostly with the father of the baby. The mother's role is that of caring for the baby and herself before and after the *Brit Milah*. The mother also begins the ceremony by handing the baby to the *Kvatter* (Godfather), thus indicating her consent for what is about to happen. As far as the *Brit Milah* ceremony is concerned, her job is to advise only. It can be very emotional for the mother to witness her newborn son undergo a surgical procedure at such early age. Family and friends or hired help are expected to do all of the preparation of food and cleanup. A festive table is set with Kosher food and wine, Challah, and a Kiddush cup is set aside to be used for all special occasions in the baby's life.

The mother of the baby may attend the ceremony or may choose to remain in another room, accompanied by friends, during the actual procedure.

# THE GODPARENTS

Traditionally two people receive the honor of being named Godparents at the *Brit Milah* or *Bris* . The role of the Godparents does not include the responsibility of raising your child in the event of your passing. It is a symbolic honor to be named Godparents and you may choose whomever you wish to honor in this way. Since their role is considered ceremonial, there is no legal obligation connected with this honor unless you make those arrangements legally.

Grandparents, relatives, and friends should be invited to participate in this special occasion. The baby's grandparents are usually selected to have the honor of being the *Kvatter* (Godfather) and *Kvatterin* (Godmother).

The *Sondak*, a righteous, honorable person, is often the grandfather; however, it can be whomever you select. This role is a great honor. The *Sondak* may also be the *Kvatter*. It is customary to choose someone who is very close to the family for these honors. (In many families, the *Sondak* and the *Kvatterin* will have future responsibilities to help with the religious training of the child).

As the ceremony begins, the godmother will receive the baby from the mother and carry him to the godfather. The godfather will carry the baby to the father, who places the baby on the chair of Elijah the Prophet. After a blessing is recited, the father takes the baby and places him in the lap of the *Sondak*, who may share Elijah's chair. The circumcision is performed while the baby is resting in the lap of the *Sondak*.

The first cup of wine is given to the *Sondak*, then each person drinks a taste of the wine. The wine cup is given to the baby's mother, so she can share in the cup of joy. Then there is a Torah benediction and a joyous meal follows in celebration. Discuss the arrangements for your son's *Brit Milah* with a *Mohel* and your rabbi, as well as friends and family.

# THE PROPHET ELIJAH

According to tradition, Elijah is seen as the guardian angel of the *Brit Milah*. Elijah attends each *Bris* to safeguard the baby during the ceremony. Elijah will be the messenger to announce the coming of the Messiah. Elijah is also considered to be Israel's constant companion and protector. At the *Bris*, a chair is placed for Elijah, a chair that is shared with the *Sondak* during the *Bris* ceremony.

# BRIT MILAH BLESSINGS AND PRAYERS

The blessings that are part of the *Brit Milah* ceremony include the *Kiddush* (the blessing over the wine), the *Misheberach* (the Jewish prayer for health), and the baby is also blessed with the reciting of the *Birkat Kohanim* (the Priestly Blessing). In some traditions, everyone recites the *Shehecheyanu* blessing together at the end of the ceremony, the blessing that gives thanks to G-d for sustaining us and allowing us to reach this precious moment. Your *Mohel* will guide you in the proper ceremonial procedures for your *Brit Milah*.

# WHAT IS A WIMPLE?

A *wimple* (a Yiddish word) is a linen wrap or swaddling cloth in which the baby is wrapped during the *Brit Milah*. This custom is observed by Jews of Western European origin. The *wimple* is later cut in long strips about six inches wide and decorated or embroidered, often with the blessing, "May he grow to attain a life of Torah, *Chuppah* and a life of good deeds." The wimple is traditionally used to bind the Torah on special occasions through-the child's life when he is called up to the Torah, at his *Bar Mitzvah* and wedding. The *wimple* may be presented at the synagogue on his first birthday. Old wimples have been found in synagogue archives.

The wimple provides a special opportunity to involve family and friends in creating and decorating the baby's wimple.

# PIDYON HABEN

According to Jewish belief, every first-born male child belongs to G-d. *Pidyon HaBen* (Redemption of the Son) is the ritual in which Jewish parents symbolically redeem their first-born son. The Torah tells us that the first male child offspring that opens the womb, belongs to G-d for a life of religious service in the temple in Jerusalem. Exodus 13:1 states, "And the L-RD spoke unto Moses, saying: 'Sanctify unto Me all the first-born, whatsoever openeth the womb among the children of Israel, both of man and of beast, it is Mine.'" Also in Numbers 18:15-16, a description of the redemption ritual is discussed.

The *Pidyon* ritual today generally involves the father of the child paying five silver dollars to a Kohen, a member of the priestly tribe. At the *Pidyon HaBen* ceremony, held when the baby is 31 days old, the baby's father will recite a special blessing, *Al Pidyon Haben*, followed by the *Shehecheyanu* blessing. The father is asked if he would prefer the money or his child; however, it is essentially a rhetorical question. The father hands the money over to the *Kohen*, who then prays for the child and recites the traditional priestly blessing. A festive meal is held as part of the ceremony.

The *Pidyon Haben* is only done if the child is the first-born male child of his mother. The first-born sons of *Kohanim* or *Levites* are exempt from this ritual. Also, if a woman has suffered a miscarriage or gives birth by cesarean section, the *Pidyon Haben* is not required.

*L'Mazeltov*

# CHAPTER TWENTY-THREE
## "Simchat Bat" or "Brit Chayim"

*"You have the opportunity to be very creative in planning your Brit Chayim ceremony."*

## BABY NAMING CEREMONY FOR A GIRL

It is customary to have your baby naming ceremony at the first *Shabbat* closest to the birth. When a baby girl is born, she is already in the covenant at birth. She is "complete when born." For baby girls, a lovely ceremony called a *Brit Chayim, Brita,* or *Simchat Bat* is celebrated. It is a celebration to welcome the baby girl and give her a Jewish name at the Torah reading. *Brit Chayim* means Covenant of Life; *Simchat Bat* is a celebration of a daughter. Welcoming your new daughter to the Jewish nation insures that she will be a vital partner in improving our world and preserving the concept of Tikkun Olam. These names essentially refer to the same ceremony that can be customized to suit your family.

Many people schedule a baby naming to be held at a synagogue followed by a kiddush or luncheon. You can choose to design your special ceremony to be held at home or do a combination of both. This is an opportunity for you as parents to work together to create a beautiful welcoming for your new baby girl. The baby naming can be done by proxy; the baby or the parents do not have to be present for the baby naming ceremony.

The *Brit Chayim* is a lovely, fulfilling and meaningful way to express joy and gratitude for the cherished gift of a new daughter. It is a *Mitzvah* to bring a daughter, as well as a son, into the world. You have the opportunity to be very creative in planning your *Brit Chayim* ceremony. Some people include a candle lighting ceremony followed by the *Shehecheyanu* prayer. A beautiful meal in honor of your daughter can be prepared and shared with family and friends. Your ceremony can include the *Kiddush* recited over the wine, followed by blessings for your new daughter—blessings for a good and healthy life. Blessings for the matriarchs, Sarah, Rebecca, Leah, and Rachel, may also be recited. Family and friends can offer blessings and prayers for your daughter that she will be faithful to G-d, be dedicated to Torah and *Mitzvot*, enjoy the blessings of Chuppah and keep her safe from harm. It is a special opportunity to give thanks, to honor the birth of your child and to welcome your daughter into your community.

Family and friends may want to give gifts such as a baby blanket, a naming certificate or special plaque in honor of your daughter's *Brit Chayim*.

# CHAPTER TWENTY-FOUR

# Jewish Baby Naming

*"The name you choose is symbolic of your love and aspirations for your child."*

## THE SIGNIFICANCE OF THE JEWISH NAME

Baby girls are named at the Brit Chayim Ceremony and baby boys are named at the *Brit Milah* Ceremony.

Selecting the right name for your child is a big responsibility. Taking into account personal attributes and qualities regarding personality, mannerisms, and nature are to be considered.

*"Each person has three names—one that his parents give him, one that others call him and the name that he acquires for himself."*
—*ECCLESIASTES RABBAH*

Stories in the Bible give many examples of the power of a name in defining a person or establishing their identity. In the Bible, Avram moves towards monotheism and the leadership of the Jewish people later in life, and G-d changes his name to Abraham,—Father of the

Multitudes. G-d also changed Jacob's name to Israel in Genesis 32:28. In both cases, the new name holds more power.

*"The earned name is worth more than the given name."*
—ECCLESIASTES RABBAH

Some Jewish parents at the time of their child's birth may want to acquire a new meaningful name for themselves. This can be done at any point in your adult lives, but it is especially meaningful when you give birth.

The ultimate decision of a baby's name is left to the parents. The controversy over the choice of a name should not mar the joy of naming the child. Choose a name with a high degree of sensitivity. Your baby will carry the name he or she is given for a lifetime. The name you choose is symbolic of your love and aspirations for your child. You may want to name your baby after a praiseworthy person, or use a name with a particular meaning.

*"He counts the numbers of the stars; He gives a name to each."*
—PSALMS (147:4)

Jewish tradition emphasizes the importance of choosing a good name and a respected name for your child. The naming of your child should be taken seriously. Jewish tradition believes that a person's name is their badge of honor, one that your child will grow to represent as the baby becomes a respected person in his or her own right. Jewish tradition believes that it is the parents' right (not grandparents or other relatives) to name the baby. It is the parent prophecy from heaven to choose the right name for their new baby. A Jewish name for a boy or a girl is given to nurture the soul and dignity of each child.

# "A good name is preferable to great riches."
## —PROVERBS 22:1

Traditions vary regarding the naming of babies. Some families, according to the customs and traditions of the family, are more inclined to use Yiddish names rather than Hebrew names. In Ashkenazi tradition a baby is often named after a relative who has passed away, as a way of honoring that person and keeping that name and memory alive. Those following Sephardic, Iberian or Oriental customs are more likely to name their babies after a living relative. Some families will name a child both a Hebrew (or Yiddish) name and an English name, often finding a link between the two names either in the meaning of the name or in the sound or the beginning letters of the names (For example: Sheila in English and Shula in Hebrew). Naming traditions are personal. What is important is that you, together as parents, follow your heart and choose a name that will honor your child, your family and your traditions.

# "A good name is better than fine oil."
## —ECCLESIASTES 7:1

Your Hebrew name will be written differently from the way your English name normally reads. Your Hebrew name will be written with your first name first followed by *ben* for a boy or *bat* for a girl, then followed by your father's first name in Hebrew and your Mother's first name in Hebrew. For some, it is important that the mother's name come first and then the father's name. For example, Sarah and Yacov's son David would have his name read as: David ben Yacov v'Sarah. In this case, the father's name was listed first.

The "v" sound in Hebrew is written using the Hebrew letter "vav", which means "and." "Ben" means son or son of, and "bat" means daughter of.

Michael and Hannah's daughter Ilana's name would read: Ilana bat Hannah and Michael.

Your child's Hebrew name will be used for his or her Bar or Bat Mitzvah and at their marriage ceremony. It is also used on their Ketubah (Jewish marriage document) and when your child is called to the Torah.

Traditionally, during the Misheberach (blessing for the sick), the person's name and his or her mother's name are called. When a person comes up to the Torah for an Aliyah, his name and his father's name are called. Check with your Rabbi on the specifics generally used in your community.

*"There are three crowns. The crown of Torah, of priesthood and of royalty. But the crown of a good name exceeds them all."*
—Pirkei Avot

## LIST OF COMMON JEWISH NAMES

Some families prefer Biblical names. Daniel, David, Michael, Benjamin, Yoel (Joel in English), and Eli are common Biblical names for boys. Ruth, Rachel, Devorah, Naomi, Dina, and Esther are common Biblical names for girls. Hebrew names may or may not have identical name counterparts in English. It's considered a *Mitzvah* to give your child a Hebrew name either in conjunction with an English name or on its own.

*The following are some Jewish names for baby boys:*
Adam – *humankind, man*
Ari – *lion*
Ariel – *lion of G-d*
Aharon – *mountain of strength*
Benjamin or Benyamin – *son of my right hand*
Chaviv – *beloved*
Daniel – G-d *is my judge*

*L'Mazeltov*

Dov – *bear*
Elan – *tree*
Jonathan or Yonatan – *G-d is given*
Joshua or Yehoshua – *G-d is my salvation*
Michael – *Who is like G-d*
Tamir – *tall like a date tree*

**The following are some Jewish names for baby girls:**
Ariela – *lioness of G-d*
Aviva – *Spring*
Dahlia – *the bow of a tree*
Deborah, Devorah – *a bee* or *to speak kind words*
Dina, Dinah, Deena – *judgment*
Ilana – *the tree*
Leora – *my light*
Hannah or Chana – *grace, gracious or merciful*
Michelle or Michaelle – *who is like G-d*
Naomi – *pleasant*
Sarah or Sara – *like a princess*
Shira – *a song*
Talya – *dew* or Tali, *my dew*
Tamar – *date tree*

# CHAPTER TWENTY-FIVE

# Family and Community

*"You shall rise before the aged
and show honor to the elder."*
—LEVITICUS 19:32)

## THE ROLE OF GRANDPARENTS

*"Gray hair is the crown of glory. It is
attained by a life of righteousness."*
—PROVERBS

Traditionally in Jewish culture, grandparents hold a place of respect as the foundation of a family's Jewish tradition and history as well as a source of wisdom and knowledge. They are invaluable as resources for Jewish continuity and connection to our history. Grandparents can be a unifying and supportive force in a growing family. Grandparents are in a special position of reverence and honor and, although they generally have little to do with the daily care of their grandchildren, they can provide the children and grandchildren with a sense of "rootedness," of belonging and a connectedness to their family, their past, their heritage, their customs and traditions. They can play an important role in shaping a grandchild's Jewish memories while helping to create strong, positive Jewish identities. Rabbis speak in praise of grandparents and Jewish tradition teaches us to honor our elders and those who have come before us.

Grandparents are a special addition to a child's life. They can foster a real sense of commitment and love of Judaism with their personal experiences by telling stories, singing songs, reading to the grandchildren, sharing dances and, most importantly, sharing the gift of their time.

For those whose grandparents are no longer living or for those who do not have grandparents living nearby, it is possible to "adopt" spiritual grandparents who can infuse your family with all the warmth, connection to tradition and wisdom grandparents can bring to a family and to the younger generation.

Pregnancy can be a time of renewal, bringing with it a variety of changes in family dynamics. In the name of *Shalom Bayit*, family harmony, pregnancy is a great excuse to repair relationships and bring your family closer together.

## *"Honor thy Father and thy Mother."*
### —*Exodus 20:12*

The fifth commandment, *"Honor thy Father and thy Mother,"* does not mean that you will always agree with or love your parents. It does ask you to show respect and to recognize their importance. Your parents raised, nurtured, and brought you into this world.

Remind yourself that no one is perfect. All parents make mistakes. As much as we wish to be the perfect parents, we will make some mistakes. Don't hold it against your parents. Honoring and respecting them elevates you as individuals.

During this time, you can decide together how each grandparent wishes to be called. Some grandparents will choose the Yiddish names *Bubbe* (grandmother) and *Zayde* (grandfather), while others may choose to use the Hebrew names for grandmother and grandfather, *Savta* and *Saba*. Give them the respect they deserve by allowing them to choose the name they most prefer.

# JEWISH FOLK CUSTOMS

*"One should not believe in superstitions,*
*but it is best to be heedful of them."*
—THE BOOK OF THE PIOUS, SEFER HASIDIM

Jewish superstitions have existed for centuries as remedies, preventative cures, and to provide protection and safeguard people from the evil eye. Superstitions are connected to all aspects of life including fertility, pregnancy, birth, illness and death. Some of those superstitions have survived and are now seen as part of Jewish folk customs. Variations of these customs can be found from one community to another. Here are some popular folk customs you have probably encountered related to the birth of a new baby and a few other common superstitions.

Amulets, protective artifacts of metal, parchment and paper, have been found in Jewish homes around the world for centuries. Various texts, including Kabbalistic texts, provide specific instructions on writing and using the amulet correctly. Please note that Mezuzot and Teffilin, whose use comes specifically from Biblical passages, are not considered to be amulets nor should they be used as amulets.

## WHAT IS A HAMSA?

The word Hamsa is derived from the Semitic word for "five" and corresponds to Hamesh (5) in Hebrew. The Hamsa is very popular in Israel. The symbol of the Hamsa as an amulet in Jewish folk art represents "the hand of G-d" and is designed to bring forth blessings, G-d's protection and to ward off evil. It has been suggested that the Hamsa with the fingers raised upward is for bringing good luck to you and a Hamsa with the fingers facing downward is designed to keep the evil eye/bad luck from coming to you. You can place a Hamsa on a wall in your home, wear it as jewelry in the form of a necklace or earrings, or carry it on a key chain.

The Hamsa is a symbol of blessings and protection. Some of the Hamsas have Hebrew words inscribed on the amulet. These include the Hebrew words of Osher (happiness), B'riut (health), Hatzlaha (success), Ahava (love), Mazal (luck), Simchah (happiness) and Pirion (fertility).

These customs are often preserved with emotional fervor in many families and no book discussing the birth of a Jewish baby would be complete without some mention of them. Keep in mind, though, that the customs listed below are only folk customs; they are not religious laws.

Some popular folk customs or superstitions used to offer protection for a safe birth and a healthy baby and to protect the new baby include:

1. Not boasting about the baby before or after the birth.
2. Not having a baby shower prior to the baby's birth.
3. Not telling the baby's name before the birth.
4. Not preparing the baby's bedroom or buying or setting up baby furniture prior to the baby's arrival.
5. Putting a red ribbon or garlic on a baby's crib.

## Kein Ayin Horah

The saying in Yiddish *Kein Ayin Horah*, which translates to "no evil eye" is used to ward off potential harm (the evil eye) in almost any situation. It is most often used when something positive or complimentary has been said, such as "he's such a beautiful baby . . . *keinahora*." "She's such a healthy child . . . *keinahora*." "The pregnancy is going very smoothly, *keinahora*." The hope is that if saying something positive has somehow created an opportunity for the evil eye to come forward and cause something bad to befall the child (or anyone), saying *keinahora* will work to keep the evil eye away. Its use is similar to the folk customs of spitting three times (or saying "*peh-peh-peh*") or throwing salt over your shoulder in an attempt to keep the evil eye away or something bad from occurring. The pronunciation of *keinahora* can vary depending on a family's Yiddish dialect and in Hebrew evil eye would be pronounced *ayin ha'ra.*

Jewish quotes, prayers, blessings, biblical quotations and *Kabbalistic* abbreviations for health, fertility, success, and safety can be added to enhance an amulet. *Elohim yishmor,* "May G-d guard thee" from Psalms 121:8 is a saying of protection to keep one safe and can be found on amulets or said as a prayer.

*"The L-rd shall guard your going out and your coming in."*
—PSALMS 121:8

## RAISING A JEWISH CHILD

What does the Talmud tell us about raising a Jewish child? The Talmud specifies *three* obligations for raising a Jewish child. The following are the three obligations:

1. The obligation to teach your child the Torah.
2. The obligation to teach your child a trade.
3. The obligation to teach your child how to swim.

**Are you surprised by these three obligations?**
Think about the definition of an obligation: An obligation can be legal or moral. The synonym for obligation is duty and responsibility. An obligation is a binding power of a promise, commitment, oath or vow.

*"And thou shalt do that which is proper and good in the eyes of the L-rd."*
—DEUTERONOMY 6:18

The Talmud's first requirement is for parents to teach their children the Torah. The Torah is Jewish Law and refers to the first Five Books of Moses (Genesis, Exodus, Leviticus, Numbers and Deuteronomy). The Torah instructs parents to teach your children Jewish values and behaviors, to teach your children responsibility and history, and to preserve our traditions and rituals.

*"The beginning and end of Torah is performing acts of lovingkindness."*
—TALMUD

The Talmud's second requirement is the obligation for parents to teach their children a trade. This requirement talks to parents in a broader sense about helping their children learn to support themselves. Teaching your child a trade represents helping your child decide how they will make their mark as they move forward in their lives, and how they can be independent and resourceful as they move into adulthood on a very practical level.

The Talmud's third requirement is the obligation to teach your children how to swim. The obligation to teach your child how to swim represents teaching your child the practical skills of safety and survival, of being prepared, planning ahead, knowing one's limitations and taking precaution. Teaching your child to swim is an empowering life lesson that involves a commitment to learning a task and developing important skills. It is also a character-building lesson on the value of follow through and preparedness. Each skill that we acquire enhances our ability to survive and thrive in the world.

These are very practical aspects to teaching your children basic life skills.

*"Who is ignorant? He who does not educate his children."*
—TALMUD

# CHAPTER TWENTY-SIX

# Being a Jewish Parent

*"Silent teaching, feelings, and gestures
are more important than exact
words or lessons."*

## A POSITIVE ROLE MODEL

Teaching the Torah is part of nourishing the child's roots. By teaching a trade, we are strengthening the child's wings. Finding the balance between roots and wings is not an easy task. When my kids were young, I was concerned that they were getting "mushy brains" by watching too much TV. So, I instituted a "TV/reading ratio." For each hour of reading, they earned a half hour of TV. There are no exact rules that we can follow, because each child has different needs and personality. But, with a lot of love and prayers, we can do a great job.

What does it mean to be a Jewish parent? Raising a Jewish child is a major responsibility and although your synagogue, Jewish Community Center and Jewish summer camps will influence your child, you are your child's most important teacher.

Raising a Jewish child has more to do with how you behave than with words alone. My husband always says that "talk is cheap." Being a Jewish parent means being a positive example of how one should live life and treat others. Envision the kind of person you would like your child to become and then be that kind of person as a role model for your child to emulate. The list of *mitzvot* provide us with guidelines for being better people, for being thoughtful, and for acting honorably. For example, "welcoming a stranger" is a *Mitzvah* that teaches us to be aware of those around us, who may be in need of assistance.

It's a challenge to be good Jewish parents in today's world. Silent teaching, feelings, and gestures are more important than exact words or lessons. Be sensitive to the great responsibility and awesome power that you possess in creating your child's physical, emotional and spiritual environment.

A few tangible ways to promote a positive atmosphere in your home can include:

- Listen to each other and your child with respect.
- Be sensitive, loving and responsive to each other.
- Take the higher ground. Be an active example of a righteous person, i.e. be willing to be the first to apologize.
- Actively and frequently express your love and appreciation of each other and your child through your words and actions.
- Be patient and understanding; speak calmly and with compassion.
- Together as a family give thanks for the blessings in your life.
- Acknowledge those around you for their kindness, assistance, achievements, wise judgments and good deeds.
- Bless your child on *Shabbat* and at bedtime so your child feels and hears love and caring coming from both of you.
- Spend time together actively interacting, reading together, sharing your day's events, doing a project and taking walks.

*"The more Torah, the more life.*
*The more study, the more wisdom.*
*The more counsel the more understanding.*
*The more charity, the more peace."*
—Pirkei Avot 2:7

## THE EMOTIONAL ATMOSPHERE
## IN YOUR HOME

*"Words that come from the heart,*
*enter the heart."*
—Chazal

Your home provides the best and most positive atmosphere for your child's emotional and spiritual growth.

Rabbis say that parents are G-d's surrogates on earth. Parents exemplify love and compassion for their offspring. A positive, loving supportive Jewish home will make your child feel loved and more secure, and promotes a sense of belonging.

There is a relationship between home and basic trust. Basic trust is the groundwork for a solid, mature identity. The quality of that trust is nurtured and nourished by the relationship between parents and child. A profound sense of trust in life can lead to a foundation of spiritual trust, which can enhance a child's sense of wholeness. The word for wholeness in Hebrew is *Shalem*, which is directly linked to the word *Shalom*, which means peace. Being at peace with oneself is the greatest gift we can help our children to שלום develop in life. Creating an emotional and spiritual environment that is warm, loving, inviting and safe helps form a solid foundation for a child, helping them trust themselves and the world around them. Part of a spiritual foundation includes an awareness of a presence of someone or something greater than ourselves. This awareness can help establish a sense of well-being and peace for children, helping them feel connected to G-d, to G-d's love and knowledge that they are an integral and vital part of G-d's world.

*"whoever destroys a single life*
*it is as if they have destroyed an entire*
*world, and whoever saves a single life*
*it is as if they have saved an entire world."*
—TALMUD

## EACH BIRTH IS SACRED

Our tradition teaches us that each birth is a blessing and each birth is a sacred event, blessed by G-d.

*"I will bless you greatly and increase your*
*offspring like the stars in the sky*
*and the sand on the shore."*
—GENESIS 22:1

Procreation involves more than sexual intercourse and conception. The Bible is not vague or evasive about procreation, the precondition for birth. And G-d is ever-present as the essential third party in the union between husband and wife.

*"Male and Female, G-d created them*
*G-d blessed them and said to them—*
*Be fruitful and multiply."*
—GENESIS 1:27-28

Each Jewish child bears the seed of our Jewish survival. Genesis states that every child is created pure in the divine image of G-d.

*"Beloved is humankind, who was created in the image of the Almighty; an abundance of love is given to each person, for each one was created in the image of G-d."*
—PIRKE AVOT 3:18

The notion that each human being is fashioned in the image of G-d implies that each child is born with a potential for love, compassion, creativity, righteousness, and mercy. You have the highest level of responsibility to raise your children so that they will develop and grow into wise, capable, responsible and compassionate adults.

## JEWISH VIEW OF THOSE WHO CHOOSE TO CONVERT TO JUDAISM

Conversion to Judaism has been part of Jewish history since Biblical times. Judaism embraces and welcomes those who choose to convert to Judaism. A person who wishes to sincerely embrace Judaism, to study and take the steps to become a Jew, is an integral and important member of the Jewish people and part of the future of our Jewish history. The Book of Ruth demonstrates that the Jewish people have a history of embracing Gerim (pronounced Ger-eem), a word that refers to converts or proselytes (one wishing to convert). Leviticus 19:34 tells us that he who travels with us, *"let him be unto you as the home-born among you. And you shall love him as thyself, for you were strangers in the land of Egypt."* Did you know that Ruth, a convert to Judaism, and her husband Boaz were the great grandparents of King David?

*"Your people shall be my people.*
*Your G-d is my G-d."*
—RUTH 1:16.

*Brit Milah* (Circumcision) is required for the man who chooses to convert to Judaism. For the adult male, the circumcision is performed in a hospital setting.

The process of conversion includes a course of Jewish studies, an appearance before a *Beit Din* (Jewish Court) and participation in a *Mikvah* (Ritual Bath). Once a convert has completed the process, he is considered to be as much a Jew as anyone who was born Jewish. In addition, it is a *Mitzvah* of self-acceptance for a convert to Judaism to consider him or herself as one who is totally Jewish, a descendent of Abraham and Sarah and our ancestors who entered into the covenant with G-d at Sinai.

*". . . thus shall they link My name with the*
*people of Israel, and I will bless them."*
—NUMBERS 6:22–27

# THE HALACHIC STATUS OF
# THE ADOPTED CHILD

In today's world, there are more Jewish couples who elect to fulfill the *Mitzvah*, "Be fruitful and multiply", and to raise a Jewish child through adoption. Adoption is a special way to build a Jewish family. We as Jewish people strongly embrace and welcome adopted children into our lives, hearts, and souls. Both the Talmud and the Bible discuss positive examples of adoption and share touching commentary about those who raise another's child. The Talmud (Sanhedrin 19b) tells us that one who raises an orphaned child as part of their family is regarded by the scriptures as if he or she was the birth parent of that child. Adopted children or those who are not Jewish at birth are considered Jews from the moment they have completed the conversion ritual. The conversion prior to the age of *Bar* or *Bat Mitzvah* consists of two parts, circumcision for boys (the *Brit Milah*) and ritual immersion (*Tevilah*) before a *Beit Din* (three rabbis), accompanied by the appropriate blessings. Boys are circumcised on the eighth day or soon after the Hebrew names are given by the adoptive parents. If you adopt an older child, a formal conversion ceremony where the child understands and participates can be observed. Your Rabbi can best advise you regarding the details and requirements. Adopted children are raised and educated as full participatory members of the Jewish people. All the *Mitzvot* and traditions that apply to a biological child, apply equally to an adopted child. After all secular and Jewish legal proceedings are completed, the child enters into the *Brit*, the covenant of the Jewish people. If a male child is not an infant but has already been circumcised, a ritual circumcision can be performed.

# CHAPTER TWENTY-SEVEN

# Sacred Jewish Concepts

*"Thou art my G-d, and I
will give thanks unto Thee."*
—*Psalms 118: 19-29*

## G-D AND JUDAISM

G-d is one. Each person is created in the image of G-d. What we see as G-d-like, therefore, exists potentially in all human beings. G-d breathed "Neshama," the Hebrew word for soul, into man and it is our soul that is at the core of our capacity to express empathy, kindness, love, and to seek justice.

In Judaism, the name of G-d written in texts is not pronounced or fully written. Within the text of L'Mazeltov, G-d is written without the "o", out of respect for all traditions. We will continue this tradition in the transliteration and Hebrew texts as well. For example, the name of G-d will be spelled A-do-nai, Shad-dai, or E-lo-him. We will sometimes refer to G-d as Ha-Shem, which is Hebrew for 'The Name".

We are sensitive to this tradition as not to desecrate the name of G-d.

*"The Ten Commandments are a symbol of
our strong belief in G-d through
faith and trust."*

# THE TEN COMMANDMENTS

*The following is a condensed version of*
*The Ten Commandments*

1. I am the L-rd, your G-d.
2. You shall have no other gods before me.
3. You shall not take the name of the L-rd your G-d in vain.
4. Remember the Sabbath day, to keep it holy.
5. Honor your Father and your Mother.
6. You shall not murder.
7. You shall not commit adultery.
8. You shall not steal.
9. You shall not bear false witness against your neighbor.
10. You shall not covet your neighbor's house, nor anything that is your neighbor's.

The Ten Commandments were given to the Jewish people on Mount Sinai. The Ten Commandments appear in the Jewish Scriptures. Many synagogues have these clearly written in Hebrew on a wall plaque. This reminds us that Moses received the Ten Commandments on two stone tablets on Mount Sinai. The first tablet, which contains the first five commandments, is symbolic of our relationship with G-d. The second tablet, which contains the last five commandments, is symbolic of our relationship with other people. The Ten Commandments are the most basic fundamental laws that teach us how we shall conduct our lives.

To believe in One G-d, to abandon old beliefs in many idols, and to have no mediators between G-d and Man are important components of the Ten Commandments. The Ten Commandments are a symbol of our strong belief in G-d through faith and trust.

G-d is all things and One—there are no idols or statues. The Ten Commandments explain the spiritual and earthly responsibility that we have as Jews. It is a guideline for taking self responsibility for our family and community. The Jewish People have the responsibility to follow the laws of the Ten Commandments and share their wisdom with the world. Many countries base their laws on the Ten Commandments.

# THE THREE COVENANTS

The *Brit Milah* is one of the three major covenants between G-d and the Jewish people found in the Torah. Abraham was commanded by G-d to circumcise all the males in his household. A *Brit* represents a physical sign of the covenant with G-d.

> *"Such shall be the covenant between Me and you and your off-spring to follow which you shall keep: every male among you shall be circumcised. You shall circumcise the flesh of your foreskin, and that shall be a sign of the covenant between Me and you"*
> —Genesis 17:10-11

The *Keshet* (Rainbow—"nature's testimony") is another sign of a covenant between G-d and the Universe which appeared after the great flood in Noah's time.

> *"When the rainbow appears in the clouds, I will remember My covenant between Me and you and every living creature so that the water shall never again become a flood to destroy all flesh."*
> —Genesis 9:12-15

The third symbol of the covenant is *Shabbat*.

> "*. . . observing the Sabbath throughout the ages as a covenant for all time: it shall be a sign for all time between Me and the people of Israel.*"
> —EXODUS 31:16-17

The *Shabbat* is a sign of the covenant representing the spiritual expression of G-d's special relationship with the Jewish people.

# THE VALUE OF MITZVOT

*"All of the six hundred and thirteen commandments are included in the Ten Commandments."*

—RASHI

A Mitzvah is one of the most fundamental principles of Jewish life. It signifies our Jewish characteristics as individuals and together as a nation.

The Hebrew root of the word Mitzvah comes from the verb "to command." Thus a Mitzvah is basically a commandment. But in common daily life, it is an expression that reflects acts of human kindness. When you help a blind man to cross the street, or when you give your seat on the bus to an elderly woman, you are doing a Mitzvah. It is not only the intention that counts. It has to be followed by an action.

Even though doing a mitzvah is a commandment from G-d, it is regarded as a privilege. We thank G-d for giving us the opportunities to do Mitzvot, and for being in a position to help others. We are also privileged and encouraged to create our own commandments, Mitzvot that reflect our moral values.

# WHAT ARE THE MITZVOT?

Jewish tradition teaches us about 613 unique Mitzvot that are mentioned in the Torah. Of the 613 commandments, 248 are positive commandments and 365 are negative commandments—you are commanded to refrain from doing certain actions. Interestingly, 248 is believed to be the number of major organs and bones in the human body, and 365 corresponds to the number of days in the solar year.

There are six Mitzvot out of the 613 that are considered constant and applicable at all times. They are:

1. Believe in G-d.
2. Do not believe in anything else other than G-d.
3. Believe in G-d's Oneness.
4. Fear G-d.
5. Love G-d.
6. Do not pursue passions of the heart or stray after your eyes.

*Here are some examples of commandments:*
- Say the Shema prayer every day.
- Honor those who teach and know Torah.
- Do not wrong a stranger in words, or in trade.
- Help the poor.
- Do not destroy the fruit trees even during a siege.
- Return a lost object.
- Do not insult or harm anybody with words.
- Do not overcharge or underpay for an article.
- Lend to the poor and destitute.
- Marry a wife by means of Ketubah and Kiddushin.
- Affix a Mezuzah on each door post.
- Do not embarrass others.
- Give respect to the elderly.
- Recite a blessing for each enjoyment.
- Wash hands before eating.
- Light the Chanukah lights.
- Read the Scroll of Esther on Purim.

Every Mitzvah is important. Even a "minor" Mitzvah will draw you into a habit of leading your life doing Mitzvot. It will nourish your heart and soul. Make it a family tradition to do at least one Mitzvah a day. Be creative with your Mitzvot. Cook a meal for a needy family, include a stranger or a lonely friend in your home for a Jewish holiday, or visit someone who is sick.

# THE BEAUTY OF TZEDAKKAH

*"The beginning and end of Torah
is performing acts of lovingkindness."*
—TALMUD

The word Tzedakkah comes from the Hebrew word Tzedek, which means justice. Giving to the poor or needy is not merely charity, it is doing what is just and right according to our Jewish beliefs. Tzedakkah is an expression of godliness in our world. Tzedakkah is a Mitzvah—a good deed or commandment and is one of the core values of Judaism. The highest level of giving Tzedakkah is giving it anonymously. Even if you don't have much to give, it is just to share what little you may have with someone who has even less.

Giving Tzedakkah is quite often an important part of celebrating a happy occasion such as the birth of a child. Making a donation in honor of a loved one's birthday, anniversary, or a special life cycle event is a lovely way to give Tzedakkah. A beautiful idea of bringing Tzedakkah into your home is to make it a part of your daily routine. You can keep a Tzedakkah box in your home, dropping a few coins every day and before *Shabbat* begins. You can purchase a Tzedakkah box in your synagogue's gift shop or make one yourself. Even a shoe box can become a great Tzedakkah box with a little imagination. Your children will love it. Every time you drop coins into your Tzedakkah box, you become aware of your positive action that promotes goodness. It is right to give Tzedakkah and it will make you feel good inside.

> *"He who gives a coin to a poor man obtains six blessings, but he who addresses him with words of comfort obtains eleven blessings."*
> —The Talmud

A Jewish tradition that is very popular is to plant a tree in Israel. We plant trees to celebrate birth and new life. Not only does it beautify Eretz Yisrael, (the Land of Israel), but it confirms your belief in the future of Israel, in those little trees that grow into large forests. We, as Jews, are a People standing in history, appreciating and preserving our past and preparing for our future.

> *"Do not separate yourself from the community."*
> —Rabbi Hillel

Tzedakkah can be a monetary donation or an act of kindness and goodness. Showing compassion and giving your time to help others is also an act of Tzedakkah. While I was a student at Tel Aviv University, I volunteered at a nearby orphanage with a couple of friends in order to do a Mitzvah. My assignment was to give attention to one baby at a time by holding the baby close to my heart for about 10 minutes. I would take one baby from his crib and go outside to the backyard and hold the baby while sitting on a swing. The Mitzvah was to provide warmth and human contact to these unfortunate babies. You cannot imagine what a satisfying experience that was for me.

*"The commandment to be charitable is in its weight as much as all the rest of the commandments in total."*

—TALMUD

## THE MEANING OF CHAI "18"

It is a traditional Jewish custom to give a donation or a gift in the amount of "Chai" or 18 or multiples of 18 such as "double Chai" = 36 or $118.00 or $180.00. Chai is two Hebrew letters, *Chet* and *Yood*, that are attached to each other. Chai = Life. Judaism gives great significance to the sanctity of life. The root word of "chai" is in the toast, "L'Chayim, to Life."

The symbol of Chai can be seen on necklaces and ornaments and is very popular in many types of jewelry. The concept of Chai is central to the Jewish People and reflects the respect of Life. The meaning of the Hebrew word "Chai" means "alive" as an action word to honor our "Living G-d." There is a Hebrew song called "Am Israel Chai"—The nation of Israel is alive and well.

## TIKKUN OLAM – REPAIRING THE WORLD

*"Judaism is an action word."*

—JEWISH SAYING

The concept of Tikkun Olam is one of Judaism's most valued gift to humanity. Tikkun Olam or "Repairing the World", as translated from

Hebrew, is part of our Jewish heritage and tradition. We are encouraged and obligated to take part, not only in our home, synagogue or neighborhood but in a more global sense, in making the world a better place for humanity.

The ideology of Tikkun Olam first appeared in the Book of Ecclesiastes and the 16th century Kabbalist, Isaac Luria, expanded on this concept in his writings. He wrote that the commitment to Tikkun Olam encompasses both the outer and innermost parts of our soul.

The still small voice within us, stirs us to take action to perfect ourselves and thus, perfect the world. Each small act of kindness has a ripple effect that yields great amounts of improvements to our environment. When we improve ourselves and our community, we are doing our part, helping G-d improve the world.

Tikkun Olam is included in the Aleinu prayer in the phrase "To repair the world under the sovereignty of the almighty". While praising G-d in this prayer we express our wishes for a better world.

Engaging in acts of Tikkun Olam plants the seeds of our survival as a Jewish People. The harvest yields improvement in our personal lives while making the world a better place for all. By liberating our own inner spark, we contribute to the good of society.

The expression "for the sake of Tikkun Olam" appears in the Mishnah as a commandment, for the sake of social justice and not because of a required law. The Jewish people have the responsibility to be "The light to all nations", to be an example for the rest of the world.

*"Thou art my G-d, and I will give thanks unto Thee."*
—Psalms 118: 19-29

You can teach your children the idea behind Tikkun Olam. Getting involved in projects such as volunteering and community service will help strengthen their character.

The creation of L'Mazeltov has been a very personal mission in my life as a mother and a nurse. It is my heartfelt goal to improve people's life in the spirit of Tikkun Olam.

# LET'S TALK ABOUT KEEPING KOSHER WHAT IS KASHRUT?

Ancient dietary laws presented in the book of Leviticus, Deuteronomy, and Codes of Rabbinic Law have given our Jewish people timeless heritage and tradition.

*Kashrut*, also known as "Keeping Kosher," has been an essential part of the Jewish life for centuries. Many believe that the laws of *Kashrut* were designed to protect the health of the early Israelites. The laws of *Kashrut* are a system for ethical living designed to connect humankind with compassion, mercy, and respect for life. By keeping a Kosher kitchen, your family has a way of preserving our tradition that is sacred to our heritage as Jews. Keeping Kosher is a *Mitzvah* that enhances the sanctity of the home. It's a topic worth discussing and thinking about. Keep in mind that one can integrate aspects of *Kashrut* into their lives by not mixing milk and meat products in the same meal, and by not eating pork or shellfish. Keeping Kosher means separate sets of dishes and utensils for cooking and storage. Fruits, vegetables and eggs are "Parve"—Hebrew for neutral; these foods can be eaten with either meat or dairy. Many ordinary foods are Kosher—you can look for Kosher symbols on the packaging of most products.

# AN INTRODUCTION TO JEWISH TEXTS

### Tanach – The Jewish Scriptures
The Tanach is the "Mikra"—"that which is read." The Tanach is comprised of twenty four books; Five books of Torah, Eight books of

Nevi'im (Prophets), and eleven books of Ketuvim (Writings). The Torah is the "Chumash"—the Five Books of Moses; it is the Law of the Jewish people. The Nevi'im are the Prophets. The Ketuvim are the Writings. Included in the Writings are Ezrah, Chronicles, and Nechemiah. The Wisdom Books include Job, Ecclesiastes, and Proverbs. The Poetry books include Psalms, Lamentations, and the Song of Solomon. Also included are the Book of Ruth, Book of Esther, and the Book of Daniel.

# TORAH — JEWISH LAW

*"Love peace, pursue peace, love people
and bring them closer to Torah."*
—PIRKEI AVOT 1:12

The Torah is the Divine Wisdom, with laws of how to act in this world. The Torah is Jewish law handed down from G-d to Moses on Mount Sinai. The Torah includes the Five books of Moses, the first five books of the Bible, Genesis, Exodus, Leviticus, Numbers, and Deuteronomy, and is written on large parchment scrolls. In a synagogue, the Torah is housed in the *Aron Hakodesh* – a Holy Ark. The first book of the Torah is Genesis or, in Hebrew, *Beresheet*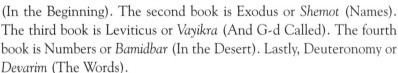
(In the Beginning). The second book is Exodus or *Shemot* (Names). The third book is Leviticus or *Vayikra* (And G-d Called). The fourth book is Numbers or *Bamidbar* (In the Desert). Lastly, Deuteronomy or *Devarim* (The Words).

According to the Talmud (Niddah 30), the baby is taught the entire Torah, while he or she is still in the mother's womb. It is the best experience in the baby's spiritual life. When it is time to be born, the child refuses to leave the womb because he or she is frightened of the outside world. G-d sends an angel to strike the child on the mouth and make him/her forget all that he/she had learned (that is why we have a little indentation under the nose, above the upper lip).

Before birth the baby is also sworn to be a Tzadik (a righteous person). He or she is born pure according to Jewish belief. Many qualities are dictated before birth but the choice to become righteous is left to our own free will. Judaism gives significance to our role as parents, to teach our children values and ethics and enhance their inborn capacity to be good.

> *"what a child says outdoors, he has learned indoors."*
> —TALMUD

## WHAT IS THE TALMUD?

The Talmud is our oral law or text, sometimes referred to as the "oral Torah," which was handed down in oral form until the second century. The Talmud consists of commentary, clarification, explanation and interpretation of our written texts. The original Talmudic writings are referred to as the Mishnah. Later, additional commentaries were added and those are referred to as the Gemara. Together they make up the Talmud. There are two Talmud texts, the Jerusalem Talmud and the Babylonian Talmud, with the Babylonian Talmud being the more extensive of the two.

## WHAT IS MIDRASH?

The Midrash is referred to as the "story behind the story." It offers more details of the stories in the Torah. *Midrash* (meaning to inquire, examine or investigate) refers to a collection of ancient Rabbinic texts that provide commentary and interpretation of the Bible and Jewish practices.

# WHAT IS KABBALAH?

The word *Kabbalah* comes from the Hebrew word *l'ka-bel*, which means "to receive", and refers to the mystical and spiritual traditions and beliefs of Judaism. The Kabbalah was founded on the teachings of the Torah and deals with the essence of G-d, Torah, creation, spirituality and humanity. The Zohar, The Book of Splendor, is an Aramaic text written in the 13th-century and is often considered the foundational text of Kabbalistic thought. Because of its depth and power, the teachings of the Kabbalah were said to have been restricted to learned Jews over the age of forty. Today there are many classes and resources that can serve as an introduction into Kabbalah.

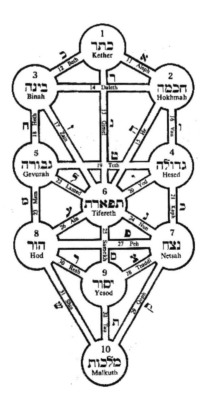

# OUR JEWISH PEOPLE'S CONNECTION TO ISRAEL

## *"If you will it, it is no dream."*
### —THEODORE HERZL

The Land of Israel is central to Judaism. The history of the Jewish People starts with Abraham and begins when G-d tells him to leave the land of his birth, promising Abraham and his descendants a new home in the land of Canaan- "The Promised Land." (Genesis Chapters 12, 13, 15 and 17). The Promised Land is described in the Torah as the "Land flowing with milk and honey…" (Exodus 3:8). "You shall clear out the Land and settle in it, for I have given you the Land to occupy it." (Numbers 33:53). The Mitzvah to live in the Land of Israel is so important that the Midrash tells us that this Mitzvah is equivalent to all other Mitzvot combined. The holiness of the Land of Israel is so powerful that many Jewish people from all over the world ask to be buried there. "One who is buried in the Land of Israel is considered as if he was buried beneath the altar." (Talmud Ketubot 111a). The Jewish connection to Israel is so profound that even one who visits the Land of Israel benefits from its holiness. The Talmud says that "one who walks four cubits in the Land, will merit a portion in the world to come." When I am in Israel, I feel so whole and complete. The Hebrew word "shalem" means wholeness, which is similar to "Shalom", which means peace. I feel such energy, intensity and contentment when I live in Israel. The sun feels hotter, the wind blows stronger, the birds chirp louder and fly faster. The dogs bark louder and run faster too. Maybe just being in Israel is being closer to G-d.

In today's times, visiting Israel contributes to the Israeli economy, as do buying Israeli products and supporting Israeli businesses. Support of Israel is crucial to its survival. To support the IDF—Israel Defense Forces contact *www.israelsoldiers.org*.

Some people commemorate their child's birth by planting a tree in Israel. The act of planting a tree represents birth, growth and renewal. Planting a tree not only enhances the beauty of an Israeli hillside; it also connects you and your family to *Eretz Ysrael*, the land of Israel. You are part of cherished tradition that continues to transform the hills of Israel into spectacular forests, one precious tree at a time. To learn more about how to plant a tree in Israel, contact *www.jnftree.org*.

Our Jewish People never gave up hope that we would return to the Land of Israel. This hope is expressed in the song- "Hatikvah" (The Hope), the anthem of the Zionist movement and the State of Israel. Theodor Herzl and Chaim Weizmann founded Zionism, the movement dedicated to the Jewish State. To make "Aliyah" to Israel is the Hebrew word for "to ascend or to go up." Aliyah is the Hebrew word for going up to read the Torah, as well as immigrating to Israel.

## WHAT IS THE DIASPORA?

Living outside of Israel is often referred to as "Galut", which is translated as Diaspora (dispersion). Jewish People who live in the Diaspora serve a very important role in the world. Jews in the Diaspora have a very positive influence on others, helping them study the Torah, doing mitzvot, and serving as Jewish role models in the community. According to the Kabbalah, the Jewish People are dispersed throughout the world, among all nations, in order to reveal and elevate all sparks of holiness that exist in the world. No matter where Jews have lived, they have dreamed and supported the Land of Israel. Israel retains its hold on our spirit no matter where we live. As Jewish people, we know in our hearts that Israel greatly matters.

# ISRAEL INDEPENDENCE DAY
# YOM HA'ATZMAUT

Israel's Independence Day is celebrated on the 5th day of Iyar of the Jewish calendar. This date coincides with the spring season during the month of May. This is the Hebrew date of the formal establishment of the State of Israel in 1948. Yom Ha'atzmaut in Israel is always preceded by Yom Hazikaron- Memorial Day for the Fallen Soldiers.

Yom Ha'atzmaut is celebrated in Israel by Israeli folk dancing and singing, going on hikes and picnics, and gathering to watch public shows. It is a special day of pride and celebration.

For Jewish People in the Diaspora, celebrating Yom Ha'atzmaut is a way to express solidarity with the State of Israel and strengthen our alliance and commitment to Israel's survival. All over the world, the Jewish community comes together for a day of celebration and support of Israel by attending festivities at synagogues and Jewish Community Centers. Israeli singing and dancing, eating Israeli foods, and attending Jewish rallies to hear Jewish speakers are some of the activities that occur on Yom Ha'atzmaut.

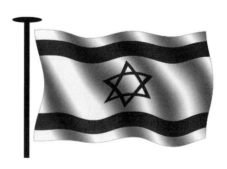

# CHAPTER TWENTY-EIGHT

# Sacred Prayers and Blessings

*"Prayer is greater than sacrifices."*
—*TALMUD*

## FROM THE ORDINARY TO THE DIVINE

Judaism is filled with beautiful and meaningful blessings and prayers. There are blessings and prayers for every occasion and occurrence in life. In Jewish tradition, honoring and praising G-d is often expressed through prayers.

*"I thank G-d for having brought me from darkness to light."*
—*FROM SHACHARIT, THE MORNING PRAYER*

It is said that the path to happiness is through gratitude. Gratitude is a key to happiness. It is only when we are grateful that we can truly know joy. Judaism is rich with blessings and prayers that express our thanks for the gifts of life we have been given —for bread, for fruit, for rainbows, for awakening, for reaching this moment in time and for so much more.

# THE SHEMA PRAYER

The Shema

שמע ישראל ה׳ אל-הינו ה׳ אחד

The *Shema* prayer is the most important and central prayer in Judaism. The *Shema* is the essence of our Jewish faith. The *Shema*, one of the first prayers we learn as children, connects us with G‑d while affirming that there is a G‑d and that G‑d is one. This prayer is the basis of Judaism. Even little children can learn the *Shema* by heart and recite this special prayer when they go to sleep at night and when they wake up in the morning.

שמע ישראל ה׳ אל-הינו ה׳ אחד

*Shma Yisrael Ado‑nai Elo‑heinu, Ado‑nai Echad*

## Hear oh Israel, the L‑rd is our G‑d, the L‑rd is one.

Within the three paragraphs of the Shema (the longer version) are the most sacred Jewish Mitzvot and principles of love of G‑d, Tefillin, Jewish education, Torah study and *Mezuzah*.

You, as parents, are the role models for your children. The concept that G‑d is a loving and compassionate G‑d is transmitted from you to your children, through your words and actions. Your warmth and affection towards them and the way you live your life will influence their character. Being the role model for your children is an awesome and honorable responsibility that belongs solely to you.

> *"He who recites a blessing*
> *is blessed himself."*
>
> *—TALMUD*

Blessings, prayers and rituals are part of daily Jewish life and an ongoing way to connect with G-d. Jewish prayer brings our awareness into focus.

It is through the use of prayer that we highlight that moment and allow ourselves to fully appreciate and honor the presence of G-d. Prayer is a passageway through which we can connect with G-d and express our reverence for life.

The act of saying a blessing connects us with G-d and the world around us by focusing our thoughts and energy. Blessings bring our awareness to the present, to that which is directly before us. Blessings mark the seasons, the events, our actions and the gifts we are about to receive. Blessings honor that which has been granted us and highlight the steps of our life's journey. Judaism has many blessings for many occasions.

Babies and toddlers can join in at an early age by learning to say "Amen" at the end of a blessing or prayer. Saying or singing *"amen"* is a fun and significant way for them to be part of the process, allowing them to feel connected to the spiritual experience you create in your home. In Hebrew, the root of the word *"amen"* comes from the verb, to believe and translates as *"it is so."*

## THE SHEHECHEYANU PRAYER

ברוך אתה ה׳ אל-הינו מלך העולם
שהחינו וקימנו והגיענו לזמן הזה

*BARUCH ATA ADO-NAI ELO-HEINU MELECH HA-OLAM,
SHEHECHEYANU VE'KIYEMANU VE'HIGIANU LAZ'MAN HAZEH*

*Blessed art thou, L-rd our G-d, Ruler of the universe, who has kept us alive and sustained us and allowed us to reach this moment.*

The *Shehecheyanu* prayer focuses our appreciation on the gift of the moment. Some examples of when to recite the Shehecheyanu prayer are tasting of a fruit for the first time in that season, the first night of a holiday, the birth of a child, or when reaching a destination after a long travel. The *Shehecheyanu* prayer celebrates each priceless, special and irreplaceable moment that has been granted to us. Shehecheyanu is basically saying, "Thank you." The Hebrew word *Todah* means "Thank you" and to be grateful to G-d for our blessings. One of my favorite Hebrew songs is called: *Todah*. My husband and I listen to it quite often. The words are very simple but meaningful.

## MODEH ANI ~ MORNING PRAYER

מודה אני לפניך מלך חי וקים
שהחזרת בי נשמתי בחמלה רבה אמנתך

*MODEH ANI LEFANEICHA MELECH CHAI V'KAYAM
SHEHECHEZARTA BI NISHMATI BECHEMLAH
RABBAH EMUNATECHA*

*I gratefully thank you, O living and eternal King, for You have returned my soul to me with compassion. Great is Your faithfulness!*

The first blessing children often learn is the *Modeh Ani*, frequently recited as a song. *Modeh Ani* is a prayer of thanksgiving and acknowledgement said immediately upon awakening each morning.

This prayer is a perfect example of elevating a seemingly ordinary event, that of awakening each morning, to a holy experience while providing an opportunity to focus, give thanks and connect with G-d.

## HAMOTZI – BLESSING OVER BREAD

ברוך אתה ה׳ אל-הינו מלך העולם
המוציא לחם מן הארץ

*BARUCH ATA ADO-NAI, ELO-HEINU MELECH HA-OLAM,*
*HAMOTZI LECHEM MIN HA-ARETZ*

*Blessed are you G-d, King of the universe,*
*who brings forth bread from the earth.*

*"Love is sweet; it tastes better with bread."*
—*YIDDISH PROVERB*

As with other blessings and prayers, *Hamotzi*, the traditional blessing over the bread is recited before we begin eating, allowing us to pause, acknowledge and give thanks to G-d for the gift of the bread we are about to eat. In this case, we are thanking G-d for the bread and reminding ourselves that this bread is a gift that was brought forth from the earth (that it didn't miraculously appear on the store shelf). There is a meditative aspect to any prayer or blessings as it clears our minds and focuses us on that which is before us, directing us to a state of gratitude and awareness.

# NETILAT YADAIM – WASHING OF HANDS

ברוך אתה ה' אל-הינו מלך העולם
אשר קדשנו במצותיו
וצונו על נטילת ידים

*BARUCH ATA ADO-NAI, ELO-HEINU MELECH HA-OLAM,*
*ASHER KIDSHANU BEMITZVOTAV,*
*VETZIVANU AL NETILAT YADAYIM*

## Blessed are you G-d, king of the universe, who sanctified us with his commandments and commanded us to wash hands.

It is customary to wash hands before we eat the bread. The blessing for the washing of the hands is called "Netilat Yadaim." When you wash hands you use a cup to pour the water three times on the right hand and three times on the left hand.

# BIRKAT KOHANIM
# THE PRIESTLY BENEDICTION

יברכך ה' וישמרך
יאר ה' פניו אליך ויחנך
ישא ה' פניו אליך וישם לך שלום

*YEVARECHECHA ADO-NAI V'YISHM'RECHA*
*YA'ER ADO-NAI PANAV ELEICHA VI'HUNEKA,*
*YISSA ADO-NAI PANAV ELEICHA V'YASEIM L'CHA SHALOM*

*May G-d bless you and keep you*
*May G-d's countenance shine upon you and*
*be gracious unto you May G-d bestow favor*
*upon you and grant you peace.*

Judaism is rich with blessings that are profound, moving, practical and spiritual. The Priestly Benediction, *Birkat Kohanim*, is no exception. Found in Numbers 6:22-27, the *Birkat Kohanim* was originally given to Moses by G-d stating that Aaron and his sons should use it to bless the children of Israel. This blessing was then recited by the *Kohanim* (the priests) over the Jewish people. This profound blessing is often used by parents to bless their children, especially on *Shabbat*.

*"To your old age I am with you. To your*
*hoary years I will sustain you; I have made*
*you, and I will carry you; I will sustain*
*you and deliver you."*
—ISAIAH 46:4

## MISHEBERACH – PRAYER FOR THE SICK

The "Misheberach" is the Jewish prayer for the sick. This prayer is said whenever someone is seriously ill and divine intervention is needed. It is often said at synagogue after the Torah reading. There are many versions of the Misheberach prayer. Here's one.

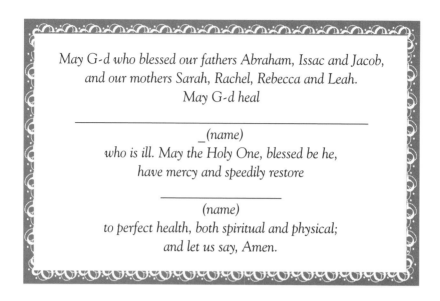

*May G-d who blessed our fathers Abraham, Issac and Jacob,
and our mothers Sarah, Rachel, Rebecca and Leah.
May G-d heal*

_____

_*(name)*
*who is ill. May the Holy One, blessed be he,
have mercy and speedily restore*

_____

*(name)*
*to perfect health, both spiritual and physical;
and let us say, Amen.*

Another, much shorter healing prayer, derives from the Book of
Numbers 12:13 when Moses beseeches G-d to heal his sister Miriam.
"Please heal her now", is the shortest prayer in the Torah.

"Heal her now, O G-d"

Numbers 12:13

# E-LO-HIM YISHMOR—G-D WILL PROTECT
## אל-הים ישמור

E-lo-him Yishmor—G-d will protect, is a Jewish saying. This saying is
mentioned in our section on amulets. You can bless a specific person
by saying "*E-lo-him Yishmor al* _____" (adding their name at
the end).

I asked my mother-in-law, Miriam, who lives in Israel, what prayers
she likes to say to bless the family and she replied—"Elo-him Yishmor
Aleinu V'Am Israel"—God will protect us and the Jewish people. She
recites this prayer every single day.

Even during trying times, the saying "*Gam Zu L'Tovah*," "Also this is for the good," supports us in trying to find a way to see all of life from a place of gratitude.

Another Jewish saying is: "Baruch Ha-Shem"—Hebrew for "Praise G-d!"

# CHAPTER TWENTY-NINE

# Jewish Symbols

*"The purpose of the laws of the Torah is to promote compassion, lovingkindness and peace in the world."*
—MOSES MAIMONIDES

## THE MEZUZAH

A *Mezuzah,* which literally means door post, is an unmistakable sign of a Jewish home. A *Mezuzah* greets us when we enter a Jewish home and is hung at eye-height on the right side of a door post, set at an angle with the top of the *Mezuzah* tilted toward the home. The *Mezuzah* casing can be made of metal, stoneware, glass or wood. Inside the casing is a Hebrew scroll, a hand-written parchment, a *klaf* inscribed with two sections from the Torah beginning with the *Shema,* Deuteronomy (6:4-9 and 11:13-21). On the reverse side of the scroll you will find the word *Shad-dai,* one of the names of G-d and an acronym for *Shomer Daltot Yisrael* "Guardian of the Doorways of Israel." The letter "ש" (shin) from the word *Shad-dai* should face the front of the mezuzah and may be visible through the *Mezuzah* casing.

A *Mezuzah* reminds us that G-d and the wonders of the universe are ever present in our lives.

Deuteronomy 6:8-9 states, "and let these things which I command you today be upon your heart . . . and write them upon the door posts of your houses and your gates." When you move to a new home, it is customary to have a ceremony with family and friends called a *Chanukkat Habayit*, dedication of the house, and *Likboa Mezuzah* meaning to "affix a *Mezuzah*." The *Chanukkat Habayit* is a ceremony that blesses your new home from the start. It is a "Housewarming" filled with Jewish meaning including the concept of kindness, charity, prayer and Torah. During this ceremony, before the *Mezuzah* is affixed to the door post, the following blessing is said:

ברוך אתה ה׳ אל-הינו מלך העולם
אשר קדשנו במצותיו וצונו לקבע מזוזה

BARUCH ATA ADO-NAI ELO-HEINU
MELECH HA-OLAM, ASHER KIDSHANU B'MITZVOTAV
V'TZIVANU LIKBO-AH MEZUZAH

*Blessed are You, O'L-rd our G-d, Ruler of the universe, who sanctifies us with holy commandments and commands us to affix a mezuzah.*

A *Mezuzah* is attached to the front entry first and then to other door posts in the home. All doorways in a home, except bathrooms, should have a *Mezuzah*. The above blessing is only said once before the front door *Mezuzah* is attached. After the *Mezuzah* or *Mezuzot* are attached, the *Shehecheyanu* prayer is recited or sung. Make sure that your *Mezuzah* is Kosher. That is, the scroll inside the Mezuzah casing is on Kosher parchment inscribed with ink by a "Sofer" (a Jewish Scribe). Check if your *Mezuzah* comes from a reliable source. Mezuzahs should be checked twice in seven years to make sure that the ink doesn't run or fade and should be checked by a Sofer or a Rabbi.

The commandment to place a *Mezuzah* on your door post creates an opportunity for doing a *Hiddur Mitzvah*, the act of beautifying the commandments. You can be very creative and artistic with the types of *Mezuzot* you have in your home. You can use your talents to design and create your own or purchase one. *Mezuzot* are available at synagogue gift shops, Judaica stores, directly from Judaic artisans and through Judaica and Israeli websites. If you know someone who plans to visit Israel, you can ask them to bring you back a *Mezuzah* made in Israel. A *Mezuzah* is a very thoughtful gift to buy for the new baby's bedroom door. The content of the *Mezuzah* contains the *Shema* prayer.

> "And these words, which I command you today, shall be on your heart: And you shall teach them diligently to your children, and shall speak of them when you sit in your house and when you walk by the way and when you lie down and when you rise up. And you shall bind them as a sign on your hand, and they shall be as frontals between your eyes. And you shall write them on the door posts of your house and on your gates."
> —DEUTERONOMY 6:6-9

Affixing a *Mezuzah* to your door post is basically saying: "This is a Jewish home." It reminds us of the story of Passover. When G-d inflicted the ten plagues on the Egyptians, he warned the Jews to mark the door posts of their homes, so that the angel of death would pass over these homes and would not harm them. The *Mezuzah* is a symbol of protection by G-d Almighty.

## TALLIT, TEFILLIN AND KIPPAH

*Tallit (tallis)*, *Tefillin* and *Kippot* are articles we put on ourselves to remind us of our relationship with G-d. They remind us of G-d's presence and to follow G-d's commandments. They continually serve to connect us with G-d, *Mitzvot* and G-d's commandments.

## Tallit (Tallis) – Prayer shawl

Tallit or tallis, a prayer shawl, are seen as robes of responsibility. The wearing of tallit comes from Numbers 15:38-39, where G-d commands us to wrap ourselves in a fringed garment that it may serve to remind us of G-d's commandments throughout each day. Traditional Jewish men wear a *Tallit Katan* (in Hebrew "small Tallit") under their shirt for the entire day as part of their regular attire. Traditionally, a Tallis (Ashekenazi or Yiddish pronunciation) would be made of wool and have one blue tread woven through it.

Before wearing the Tallit, the following prayer is recited:

ברוך אתה ה' אל-הינו מלך העולם
אשר קדשנו במצותיו
וצונו להתעטף בציצת

*Baruch Ata A-do-nai E-lo-heinu Melekh Ha'olam*
*Asher Kid'shanu B'mitzvotav, V'tzivanu*
*L'hit'atef Betzitzit*

*Blessed are you, L-rd our G-d, Ruler of the universe, who has sanctified us with his commandments, and commanded us to wrap ourselves in fringes.*

## Teffilin – a symbol of the covenant

*"You shall bind them for a sign upon thy hand, and they shall be for a reminder between thine eyes."*
*—Deuteronomy 6:8*

Tefillin, phylacteries, are two small black leather boxes which house small pieces of parchment inscribed with the *Shema* and three other

Biblical passages. They are traditionally worn by men when *davening* (praying) morning prayers during the week. Tefillin are ritualistically wrapped around the left hand and arm, and around the head. The Book of Jewish Education (*Sefer HaChinuch*) says the *Mitzvah* of donning Tefillin is one of the Mitzvot that helps protects us against sin. The placement of the Tefillin is designed to link our heart, hand and mind together while reconnecting us with G-d. This practice is one that again serves to focus our awareness and unite us with G-d.

## KIPPOT

## *"A Blessing on your Head."*

A *kippah* (Hebrew) or *yarmulke* (Yiddush) is a head-covering, a skullcap worn by Jews. Wearing the *kippah* is considered to be an act of *Kiddush Ha-Shem*, of Sanctifying the holy name of G-d. The *kippah* is a symbol of pride. When you wear a *kippah*, you are basically saying that you are proud to be a Jew. Wearing a *kippah* is mentioned in the Talmud (Kiddushin 31), which states that the *kippah* is worn as a reminder that the Divine Presence of G-d (the *Shekhinah*) is always above us overhead.

# THE MENORAH

The Menorah is one of the oldest symbols of the Jewish People. This seven branched symbol was used in the Temple. Traditionally, the Menorah is a symbol to be, "A light unto the Nations" (Isaiah 42:6). The "eternal light", called in Hebrew Ner Tamid, is the continuous light or eternal flame that symbolizes the Menorah.

On Chanukah, we light the Chanukiah, which is an eight branch Menorah plus a shamash branch (a helper candle). The Chanukiah is similar to the seven branched Menorah. Chanukah celebrates the historical miracle that one day's oil lasted for eight days.

A Menorah is a great gift idea with special symbolism and tradition to the Jewish people.

## MAGEN DAVID — "STAR OF DAVID"

The Magen David is Hebrew for the "Star of David," which is the most common Jewish symbol in modern times. There are various opinions on the significance of this symbol.

The Magen David became very popular as the emblem of the Zionist movement in 1897. The Magen David is proudly displayed on the flag of the State of Israel and it is also the symbol for Red Magen David, which is the equivalent to the Red Cross in Israel.

The Magen David, "Star of David", is very popular in jewelry and ornaments and makes a great gift.

# Chapter Thirty

# The Beauty of Shabbat

*"Shabbat can be a special and
sacred time together as a family."*

## BABY'S FIRST SHABBAT

On the occasion of a baby's first *Shabbat*, the parents along
with their baby may be called to the Torah to receive a
blessing after the Torah portion has been read. The baby's
first *Shabbat* is a joyous opportunity to make it very special
and meaningful for you and your family.

The baby's first *Shabbat* is a happy occasion and is often
celebrated with a festive *Shabbat* meal either on Friday night, or
on Saturday afternoon after services at the synagogue.

## OVERVIEW OF SHABBAT OR SHABBOS

*"Come my Beloved, to meet the Bride;
Let us welcome the Shabbat."*

—Shabbat Prayer

It has been said that Jews don't make or keep *Shabbat* so much as *Shabbat* makes or keeps us Jews.

We can all thank Judaism for bringing us the concept of the weekend, the idea that we need a day of rest. G-d took the Jews out of Egypt, where they were enslaved and didn't have any day of rest. A day of rest is a symbol of freedom. This humanitarian concept is expressed in Jewish law, instructing owners and employers to give their workers a day of rest, too. It is also interesting to note that we are instructed to give the earth time to rest. It is a Jewish custom to work the field for six years and let it rest on the seventh year.

Prior to sunset, a Jewish family prepares for the most important Jewish holy day, called in Hebrew *Shabbat*, (Sabbath). The *Shabbat* has the unique status of being the only holy day mentioned in the Ten Commandments and the only holy day included in G-d's first and most fundamental ethical requirements. The *Shabbat* is considered to be Judaism's most important ritual observance. The essence of *Shabbat* is *being* rather than *creating*.

This special day is one that includes three important characteristics of *Kedushah* (holiness), *Menuchah* (rest), and *Oneg* (joy).

*Shabbat* can be a special and sacred time together as a family by going to synagogue together, sharing a Sabbath meal, or enjoying a walk in the park.

It is traditional to prepare food ahead of time. A delicious stew called cholent or chamin is a popular food that cooks overnight for *Shabbat*.

For those of you who are observant or wish to become observant, there is a way to enjoy a hot and nourishing meal on the Sabbath. Since Jewish law prohibits lighting a fire and cooking on *Shabbat*, cholent or chamin (in Hebrew) has been the answer for centuries in Jewish homes all over the world. There are a great variety of cholent recipes and you can find one of them in our recipe section.

*"Remember the Shabbat to keep it holy."*
*—Exodus 20:8*

# KABBALAT SHABBAT
# WELCOMING THE SHABBAT

If you haven't yet started to light the *Shabbat* candles, you can begin now, while you are pregnant. Lighting the candles symbolizes the "spark of life" within you and the new little soul on-board. *Shabbat* nurtures the family like a mother nurtures her children. Lighting the candles bring "Shalom Bayit"—Light and Peace to your home. *Shabbat* is a family weekly retreat—a time for coming together as a family.

The *Shabbat* begins at sunset each Friday evening. In Jewish tradition, each day starts at sundown and ends at sundown of the following day. The exact time of sundown varies according to the season and where you live. Jewish calendars will often provide the times of the sunset.

Young girls starting at the age of three years old can start lighting the *Shabbat* candles. *Shabbat* officially begins with the lighting of the Sabbath candles, which is generally done by the women in the home 18 minutes before sunset on Friday evening. The lighting of the candles is followed by the blessing over the candles. After lighting the candles the woman (or women) of the home circles her hands over the flames three times symbolically welcoming in the Sabbath. She then covers her eyes with her hands while saying the *bracha* or blessing. Two different reasons for covering one's eyes while saying the blessing have been suggested. One reason is to avoid seeing or enjoying the candles burning until after one has recited the blessing, acknowledging and thanking G-d for the gift of the Sabbath. The other reason suggests that we close our eyes in order to recite the blessing in a more focused and meditative way in order to internalize the *Shabbat* spirit. A woman has the opportunity to ask G-d for blessings as she lights the *Shabbat* candles.

Your *Shabbat* candlesticks can be a very decorative addition to your household. You can have more than one set of *Shabbat* candlesticks.

ברוך אתה ה׳ אל-הינו מלך העולם אשר
קדשנו במצותיו וצונו להדליק נר של שבת

*Baruch ata Ado-nai Elo-heinu Melech ha-olam,*
*asher kidshanu bemitzvotav ve-tsivanu*
*lehadlik ner shel Shabbat*

Blessed are You, L-rd our G-d, King of
the universe, who sanctified us with his
commandments and commanded us to
kindle the sabbath candles.

## BLESSING YOUR CHILDREN

Before dinner, after the candle lighting, it is customary for parents to
bless their children with the following blessings. As the parents recite
the appropriate blessings, they will traditionally place their hands
above the child's head. This is a beautiful ritual that makes each child
feel cherished, valued and protected.

From an early age, they will experience a sense of the strength and
security that comes from something greater than themselves.

### FOR SONS
ישמך אל-הים כאפרים וכמנשה

*Y'simcha elo-him k'efrayim v'ki m'nasheh*

May G-d make you like
Ephraim and Manasseh.

### FOR DAUGHTERS
ישמך אל-הים כשרה רבקה רחל ולאה

*Y'simech elo-him ksarah rivkah rahel v'lei'ah*

May G-d bless you like Sarah,
Rebecca, Rachel and Leah.

יברכך ה׳ וישמרך
יאר ה׳ פניו אליך ויחנך
ישא ה׳ פניו אליך וישם לך שלום

YEVARECHECHA ADO-NAI V'YISHM'RECHA
YA'ER ADO-NAI PANAV ELEICHA VI'HUNEKA,
YISSA ADO-NAI PANAV ELEICHA V'YASEIM L'CHA SHALOM

May G-d bless you and keep you
May G-d's countenance shine upon you and
be gracious unto you May G-d bestow favor
upon you and grant you peace.

# THE SHABBAT (SHABBOS) MEAL

The *Shabbos* Meal (*Ashkenazi* pronunciation) or *Shabbat* Meal (*Sephardic* pronunciation) is a festive meal with "*Shabbat* atmosphere"—a joyous occasion made richer when celebrated with family and friends. Before the meal begins, it is very traditional and special to sing or recite *Eshet Hayil* and *Shalom Alechem*.

Eshet Hayil, "A Woman of Valor", is a twenty two verse poem from the book of Proverbs, which is recited by a woman's husband on Friday evening. It is a tribute to a man's wife and a profound expression of gratitude for all that she has done for him and what she means to him. When my husband sings Eshet Hayil to me, he makes me feel very cherished and loved and I appreciate it very much.

*Shalom Aleichem*, "Peace Be Upon You", is a traditional *Shabbat* song which is sung on Friday night at the beginning of *Shabbat* before the Kiddush. The song is sung with great enthusiasm and joy. The lyrics are symbolic of welcoming the angels who accompany a person home on Friday night, the Sabbath evening.

My husband grew up in a traditional, though not orthodox setting, in Tel Aviv, Israel. He told me that when he was a young boy, his father insisted the family would have a *Kiddush* and a meal together every Friday night. If the children wanted to make plans to spend time with friends, they knew they would have to wait until the meal was over, without rushing through it. While he was young he did not appreciate this rule, but as he grew older and had children of his own, he realized what a gift of togetherness he had inherited from his parents.

On *Shabbat*, enhance your joy and celebration as a family. Some families enjoy cooking, singing, cleaning or baking Challah together as they prepare their *Shabbat* dinner. *Shabbat* is an opportunity to beautify your home and table with flowers, a special tablecloth, Kosher wine, a beautiful braided Challah, *Kiddush* cups, decorations and tasty foods. This is a holiday of joy and rest . . . so celebrate, give thanks, relax and enjoy!

# THE SHABBAT BLESSINGS

### The Kiddush

The word *Kiddush* means sanctification. The following *Kiddush* blessing is recited to sanctify the wine on any occasion and is said while holding up the cup of wine. The *Kiddush* blessings for *Shabbat* is longer and can be found in your prayer book.

ברוך אתה ה׳ אל-הינו מלך העולם בורא פרי הגפן

BARUCH ATA ADO-NAI ELO-HEINU MELECH HA-OLAM,
BOREI PE'RI HA-GAFEN

Blessed art Thou, Ado-nai our G-d,
King of the universe, who creates
the fruit of the vine.

## The Friday Night Kiddush

As with many Jewish prayers and blessings, the Friday-night *Kiddush* is often sung. The following is the English version of the Friday night *Kiddush*.

> *The sixth day. And the heavens and the earth and all their hosts were completed. And G-d finished by the Seventh day His work which He had done, and He rested on the Seventh Day from all His work which He had done. And G-d blessed the Seventh Day and made it holy, for on it He rested from all His work which G-d created to function.*
>
> *Blessed are You, L-rd our G-d, King of the universe, who creates the fruit of the vine. (Amen)*
>
> *Blessed are You, L-rd our G-d, King of the universe, who has sanctified us with His commandments, has desired us, and has given us, in love and goodwill, His holy Shabbat as a heritage, in remembrance of the work of Creation; the first of the holy festivals, commemorating the Exodus from Egypt. For You have chosen us and sanctified us from among all the nations, and with love and goodwill given us Your holy Shabbat as a heritage. Blessed are You L-rd, who sanctifies the Shabbat. (Amen)*

After this blessing is recited, it is customary to share a sip of wine from the *Kiddush* cup, starting with the oldest to the youngest, out of respect. As time goes by, your child will become connected to the *Shabbat* rituals, prayers and traditions.

### Blessing The Challah

Right before blessing the challah, we say the blessing for washing the hands—Netilat Yadayim (on page 182).

The blessing over the challah is said on *Shabbat* as it is before any meal where bread is served. On the *Shabbat* and other holy days, we generally say the blessing over two loaves of challah. You can find the *Hamotzi* blessing (or *Motzi*) in our section on blessings, on page 181. The blessing over the bread is followed by the special *Shabbat* meal.

## Birkat Hamazon

*"And you shall eat and you shall be
satisfied. And you shall bless G-d, your G-d,
for the good land he has given you."*
—DEUTERONOMY 8:10

The Hebrew word *Mazon* means food or sustenance. In English, *Birkat Hamazon* refers to "grace after a meal."

Following the *Shabbat* meal, it is again our obligation to pause and give thanks—to take time to focus on the blessings which have been so graciously provided. We often take food (and so much more) for granted. The *Birkat Hamazon* is a beautiful blessing of gratitude and acknowledgment. Traditionally, the full *Birkat Hamazon* is required whenever a meal includes bread and thus is begun with the *Hamotzi* blessing. The complete *Birkat Hamazon* can be found in your prayer book.

The *Birkat Hamazon* can be said or sung, as is true of most blessings and prayers in Judaism. After the *Birkat Hamazon* is said, it is traditional to continue the joyous celebration of *Shabbat* by singing together around the table. One of my fond memories of *Birkat Hamazon* was at Jewish summer camp. I was nine years old and I led the entire camp in singing the *Birkat Hamazon* Blessing. I felt so proud and honored. It was very special to be surrounded by the campers and staff, singing this beautiful melody together at the table. I carry this special memory with me always when I sing the *Birkat Hamazon* many years later!

## HAVDALAH CEREMONY

The *Havdalah* ceremony is a lovely ritual that separates the day of holiness from the everyday life. At the close of the Sabbath, once three stars have been spotted in the sky (generally about 45 minutes to one hour past sunset—nightfall), the *Havdalah* ceremony is conducted.

*Havdalah* means "separation" or "distinction." The *Havdalah* ritual transitions us from the holiness of the *Shabbat* into our normal or regular week.

> ## "You are to distinguish between the holy and the common."
> —*Leviticus 10:10*

For this service you will need a tall, braided candle with at least two wicks (a *Havdalah* candle), a *Kiddush* cup of kosher wine or grape juice and a *B'samim* box, a box filled with fragrant spices.

The following are a "medley" of verses: The *Havdalah* service begins with a verse from Isaiah 12:2-3:

> *Indeed, G-d is my salvation;*
> *I am confident and shall not fear,*
> *for G-d the L-rd is my strength and song,*
> *and He has been my salvation.*
> *You shall draw water with joy out of the wellsprings of salvation.*
> *Deliverance is the L-rd's; may Your blessing be upon Your people forever.*
> *The L-rd of hosts is with us, the G-d of Jacob is our everlasting stronghold.*
> *L-ord of hosts, happy is the man who trusts in You.*
> *L-ord help us; may the King answer us on the day we call.*
> *For the Jews there was light and joy, gladness and honor—*
> *so let it be with us.*
> *I will raise the cup of deliverance and invoke the Name of the L-rd.*

The wine is seen as a symbol of joy and we pray that the joy will continue to grow as we move into our normal weekday.

> *Blessed are You, L-rd our G-d, King of the universe,*
> *who creates the fruit of the vine.*

The blessing over the *b'samim*, (fragrant spices) follows the blessing over the wine. Smelling the *b'samin* fills us with the sweetness of the *Shabbat*.

First we say the blessing while holding the *B'samin* box in our right hand and after the blessing we smell the spices and pass them to others participating in the *Havdalah* service.

> *Blessed are You, L-rd our G-d, King of the universe,*
> *who creates various kinds of spices.*

After the blessing over the light that emanates from the *Havdalah* candle, we look at the flame as it is reflected in our fingernails.

> *Blessed are You, L-rd our G-d, King of the universe,*
> *who creates the lights of fire.*

The kiddush cup is then held in the right hand and the following blessing is recited.

> *Blessed are You, L-rd our G-d, King of the universe,*
> *who makes a distinction between sacred and profane,*
> *between light and darkness, between Israel and the nations, between the*
> *Seventh Day and the six work days.*
> *Blessed are You L-rd, who makes a distinction*
> *between sacred and profane.*

The full *Havdalah* Service with Hebrew and transliteration is found in most prayer books.

At the end of *Shabbat*, we wish our loved ones a *Shavua Tov*, a good week and we sing "*Eliyahu Hanavi.*" *Eliyahu HaNavi*, Elijah the Prophet, is a symbol of hope representing a future filled with permanent peace, freedom, and tranquility for all humanity.

# CHAPTER THIRTY-ONE

# Jewish Life Cycle Milestones

*"In a place where there are no men, strive to be a man."*

—JEWISH PROVERB

## BAR MITZVAH AND BAT MITZVAH

At the age of thirteen a boy becomes a *Bar Mitzvah* and, according to Jewish law, he is considered a man. Girls become *Bat Mitzvah* at the age of twelve. *Bar Mitzvah* literally means "son of the commandment" and *Bat Mitzvah* means "daughter of the commandment." *Bar* is the Aramaic word for son, whereas *Bat* is the Hebrew word for daughter. A young

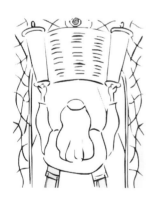

person automatically becomes Bar and Bat Mitzvah when they come of age. The real meaning of Bar and Bat Mitzvah is being responsible for following the commandments. The *Bar and Bat Mitzvah* initiates a child into adulthood and, from that point forward, they are considered to be responsible for all that would be required of Jewish adults—ethically, behaviorally, religiously and morally. They would now be considered responsible for observing the *Mitzvot*, for caring for their physical needs, for giving *Tzedakkah and Tikkun Olam*, each according to their individual ability. A *Bar* or *Bat Mitzvah* is frequently marked by the ceremony in the synagogue and a celebration following the services. Beginning on the morning of the Bar Mitzvah, the young man puts on

Tefillin and is now counted as a man in the Minyan (the quorum of ten Jews). The celebration can be a simple or an elaborate event with a "Seudat Mitzvah" (festive meal celebrating the *Bar/Bat Mitzvah*). The *Bar* or *Bat Mitzvah* ritual and celebration will vary according to family and community traditions. Your *Rabbi* will be your greatest resource as your family plans for your child's *Bar* or *Bat Mitzvah*.

## CHUPPAH AND MARRIAGE, THE KETUBAH

*"From every human being there rises a light that reaches straight to heaven, and when two souls that are destined to be together, find each other, their streams of light flow together and a single mightier light goes forth from their united being."*
—BAAL SHEM TOV

In Judaism, marriage is a holy covenant. It is a *Mitzvah* to be married and raise children. The very decision to marry implies a willingness to enter wholeheartedly into a sacred union with another person.

*"To facilitate a union between a man and a woman is as difficult a task as parting of the Red Sea."*
—TALMUD

In Yiddish the word for a perfect match, or a soulmate, is *Beshert* (*b'shert*), which literally means fate or destiny. *Kiddushin* is the Hebrew word for sanctification and is connected to the word *Kiddush*, the blessing sanctifying the wine. Both words are derived from the root of the word *Kadosh*, which means holy. Two souls joining together in marriage is considered holy. As it relates to marriage, *Kiddushin* refers to the betrothal part of the ceremony and *Nisuin* refers to the actual marriage.

A Jewish wedding ceremony is performed under a *Chuppah* (wedding canopy). A *Chuppah* can be as simple as a *Tallit*, a Jewish prayer shawl, held by friends or family members. The bride and groom will stand under the *Chuppah* during the ceremony. The bride and groom may opt to have a *Chuppah* which is more elaborate and can be decorated with flowers and fruits. The *Chuppah* is a small sanctuary which represents their new home together.

In a Sepharadic tradition, a candle lighting would mark the beginning of the wedding ceremony in order to infuse light into the celebration. The bride and groom are escorted to the *Chuppah* by their parents. Then the *Kallah* (bride) circles the *Chatan* (groom) seven times. Just as the world was created in seven days, the bride is symbolically building the walls of the couple's new world together. The number seven represents wholeness and completeness. The bride settles at the groom's right hand side. Now the Rabbi recites the betrothal blessing followed by the first cup of wine, a symbol of sanctification. At this point the groom places the ring on the bride's finger and recites the betrothal blessing:

### THE BETROTHAL BLESSING

HAREY AT MEKUDDESHET LI B'TABA'AT
ZO K'DAT MOSHE V'YISRAEL

*With this ring, you are consecrated to me
according to the law of Moses and Israel*

Now the Rabbi will read the *Ketubah* (signed prior to the ceremony under the *Chuppah*). The reading of the *Ketubah* is a break in between the *Kiddushin* and the *Nisuin* rituals of the wedding ceremony. The *Sheva Brachot* (seven blessings) are now recited and the second glass of wine is shared by the bride and groom. The ceremony is concluded with the breaking of the glass. Even during such a joyful occasion, we commemorate the destruction of the temple, by breaking the glass.

Presenting an object of value is one requirement of the wedding ritual, and in most cases the ring functions as that object of value. Other objects of value may be exchanged instead. If a ring is used, Jewish tradition designates the use of a plain gold band for the wedding ceremony. The simplicity of the band, without any breaks or adornment, allows its value to be clearly seen. On a practical level and symbolically, this is an important aspect of a wedding ceremony. In addition, the continuity of the band symbolizes the continuity of the union. *Halacha*, Jewish law, also requires the presence of two witnesses (not related to you) who would sign the Ketubah prior to the ceremony and witness the wedding ceremony under the *Chuppah*.

My son Michael and his beautiful bride, Tania, were married under the *Chuppah* in Santiago, Chile. The glow and love in Tania's eyes as she gazed into Michael's eyes while she circled around him seven times, is a heavenly memory that I will always cherish. I appreciated the common thread of Judaism during the wedding ceremony and felt so connected with our Jewish people from all over the world. Our Jewish customs and traditions connect all of us to one another worldwide. When my husband and I travel to another city or country, we always look for a local synagogue to visit. No matter where we are, we always feel like we are at home with family.

## What is a Ketubah?

The *Ketubah* is a written Jewish marriage contract which traditionally details the legal and moral commitment to marriage and is considered to be a legal document. After the ring ceremony at the wedding, the *Ketubah* is read aloud, usually by a Torah scholar who can fluently read the Aramaic text. This binding document states the principal obligations of the groom to his bride. These include the promise to provide her with food, clothing and affection, as well as other obligations. The reading of the *Ketubah* serves as a separation between the two phases of marriage—the *Kiddushin* and the *Nisu'in*.

After the *Ketubah* is read aloud, it is handed to the groom, who gives it to his bride for safe keeping. The *Ketubah* handed from a husband to a wife is symbolic of the covenant Moses wrote as the Jewish People accepted G-d at Mount Sinai.

> **The components of the *Ketubah* include:**
> The date of the wedding, the names of the bride and groom written correctly in Hebrew, and the solemn obligations of marriage. The bridegroom promises to love, honor and cherish his bride. He promises to protect her, support her, and take care of her needs prescribed by Jewish laws and traditions. The bride declares to the groom that by accepting the wedding ring, she pledges all of her love and devotion to him and takes upon the fulfillment of all of the duties incumbent upon a Jewish wife. The bride always keeps the *Ketubah* in her possession, as it is her guarantee of protection.

The practice of illuminating the *Ketubah* with decoration, making it artistic, or pleasing to the eye is optional. The *Ketubah* need not be written by a *"Sofer"*, a specially sanctioned scribe or written on parchment, in contrast to the Torah or other religious documents as it is technically considered a legal document.

# THE BEAUTY OF THE MIKVAH

Some women are returning to tradition and finding spiritual meaning in the waters of the Mikvah. L'Mazeltov seeks to raise awareness of this beautiful mitzvah for Jewish women that comes from the Torah.

# What is a Mikvah?

A Mikvah is a pool of flowing rainwater. The Mikvah is often referred to as the "ritual waters." There are naturally occurring Mikvahs in our world such as lakes and oceans. In modern days, the Mikvah is indoors, private, heated and very comfortable, like a spa facility.

The Mikvah is the center of the Laws of Family Purity—the *"Taharat Hamishpachah"*—the set of Torah laws that influence the couple's marital relations. According to the Jewish law (the Halachah), there is a strong emphasis on building a Mikvah in every Jewish community. In fact, the Mikvah is quite often the first building to be erected in a new community—it is that important.

There is utmost respect for the Jewish woman, who is the creator of new life: women conceive and give birth and give warmth and meaning to the Jewish home. Contact *www.mikvah.org* for more information.

# CHAPTER THIRTY-TWO

# Overview of Jewish Holidays

*"We, the Jewish People, have such a rich and beautiful tradition, history, values, and heritage . . . "*

## THE JEWISH HOLIDAYS

Judaism is known for the value it places on community, education and *Tzedakkah*, but even more so for the value it places on family and children. It is said that Judaism could continue to function without a synagogue, but not without family. Memories of family gatherings are inscribed in my mind from the early days of childhood. The smells, tastes, candle lights and songs became part of me for life. We encourage you to invite people into your home for a Jewish holiday. Jewish life is deeply rooted in the family and most holidays reflect that family connection. Most major Jewish holidays specifically embrace the participation of the children. On *Shabbat*, we bless the children and on Chanukah we light candles and play *driedle*. For Purim, children wear costumes, use noisemakers and sing songs as they learn about the story of Esther. On Passover, the children ask the four questions and search for the *Afikomen* after the meal. Simchat Torah's festivities are full of singing and dancing while parading with flags and apples.

# JEWISH CALENDAR

I'm sure that many of you have heard the question—"When is Rosh Hashana this year?" Every year it is slightly different. Why does it change from one year to another? Holidays are celebrated on the same day of the Jewish calendar every year, but the Jewish year is counted differently than the solar year on the Gregorian calendar that is used by most of the western world.

It is interesting to note that the Jewish calendar is based on the rotation of the earth about its axis (a day); the revolution of the moon around the earth (a month); and the revolution of the earth around the sun (a year). In contrast, the Gregorian calendar used almost everywhere in the world does not include the moon cycles. The Jewish calendar has in its year either 12 or 13 months. The lunar month on the Jewish calendar begins when the first sliver of the moon becomes visible after the dark of the moon. In ancient times, when the new moon was observed (this is called in Hebrew, *"Rosh Chodesh"*), two independent reliable witnesses would send out messengers to tell the people that a new month began.

The year number on the Jewish calendar refers to the number of years since creation, which is calculated by adding up all of the ages of people in the Bible back to the time of creation. Jewish people refer to the years before the Gregorian calendar as C.E. (Common Era) or B.C.E. (Before the Common Era).

## The Jewish calendar has the following months:
Month 1 - *Nissan* (March – April)
      2 - *Iyar* (April – May)
      3 - *Sivan* (May – June)
      4 - *Tammuz* (June – July)

5 - *Av* (July – August)
6 - *Elul* (August – September)
7 - *Tishrei* (September – October)
8 - *Cheshvan* (October – November)
9 - *Kislev* (November – December)
10 - *Tevet* (December – January)
11 - *Shvat* (January – February)
12 - *Adar* (February – March)
13 - *Adar II* (February – March)

You can find a Jewish calendar at your local synagogue and/ or Jewish community center. It's a good idea to keep one posted on the wall in your home, so you can look up Jewish holidays, and other important dates.

# FALL HOLIDAYS – THE HIGH HOLY DAYS
# ROSH HASHANA – THE JEWISH NEW YEAR

Rosh Hashana, the Jewish New Year, and Yom Kippur, the Jewish Day of Atonement, are referred to as the Jewish High Holy Days, a solemn introspective period of the Jewish calendar. The days between the two are also considered to be important holy days. Rosh Hashana falls on the first and second days of Tishrei, and Yom Kippur on the tenth of Tishrei. The High Holy Days have the greatest attendance in the synagogue compared to other days of the year.

Rosh Hashana is a very festive holiday. We traditionally eat sweet foods such as apples and honey and honey cake (see recipe section). On Rosh Hashana, we pray that the next year will be sweet and successful. During the year, we put salt on the challah when we say the *Hamotzi* blessing, but on Rosh Hashana we dip the challah in honey. The challah takes another shape during this holiday. This time we celebrate with a round challah that symbolizes the circle of life. It is also customary to buy new clothes for Rosh Hashana in honor of the New Year.

On Rosh Hashana, we offer the greeting *"Shana Tova,"* Happy New Year, and *"L'Shanah Tovah Tikatevu,"* which means, *"May you be inscribed (in the Book of Life) for a good year."* The blowing of the *"Shofar"* (curved ram's horn) in the synagogue occurs at Rosh Hashanah and Yom Kippur (except on *Shabbat*). The *Shofar* is the oldest wind instrument known to man. The piercing sound of the Shofar awakens us and evokes a sense of awe. It is a Mitzvah to be present at the blowing of the *Shofar*. It has also been said that the sound of the *Shofar* is a call to repentance.

# YOM KIPPUR – THE DAY OF ATONEMENT

Yom Kippur is the Day of Atonement. It is a solemn day dedicated to fasting, prayer and contemplation. It is a day of deep reflection and a time for forgiving and repenting. We often forget to ask for forgiveness from those closest to us, from our own children, family members, spouses and friends. Although we ask for G-d's forgiveness, we are also told that for any transgression against others, it is not for G-d to forgive. It is up to us to seek forgiveness from the individuals whom we may have harmed. Judaism understands that though we may intend to do our best, we are not perfect.

The concept of forgiveness reminds me of a story I had heard. It is a story about a boy who was very angry and was hurting others. His wise father gave him a hammer and a box of nails and told him that he could hammer the nails into the fence, whenever he felt angry. After a while, the son told his father that he didn't have the need to put any more nails in the fence. "Now", the father said, "take the nails out of the fence." When the boy finished removing the nails, his father showed him the holes that were left in the fence and explained that if we hurt someone we can apologize and ask for forgiveness, but the wounds we had inflicted will still be there.

We all need to strive to choose our words and actions so carefully as to avoid "the holes in the fence."

The eve of Yom Kippur starts with a prayer that is called *Kol Nidrei* (All Vows). This special prayer welcomes all people, those who have sinned and those who have not, to pray together for forgiveness as individuals and as a community. This prayer asks G-d to absolve us from all our vows. Jews come to the synagogue on this holiest of nights to hear this opening prayer, which is recited or sung while all are standing. *Kol Nidrei* is repeated three times. A day of fasting is observed from the evening meal before sundown to nightfall on Yom Kippur day. Jewish tradition excuses you from fasting if you have medical reasons or if you need medication or if you are pregnant or lactating. It is best to ask your Rabbi and Doctor if you are allowed to fast, and that "health comes first." The "break the fast" meal is usually a light meal shared by family and friends in the synagogue or in your home.

Yom Kippur is a time to reflect on our year, our lives, our actions and our thoughts. It is a time to do what we can to right our ways as we enter the New Year. Although Yom Kippur is a somber day, it is also one of joy. The "Yom Kippur Attitude" explains that we stand in awe of G-d's judgement, but we are confident that G-d will forgive us as he has always done. We have another chance and we are deeply grateful. At the close of Yom Kippur, the Book of Life is said to be sealed and the greeting becomes *"G'mar Tov"*—*May you finish well* or *G'mar Chatima Tova! – May you be sealed in the Book of Life.*

# SUKKOT

*"You shall dwell in the sukkah seven days."*
—*Leviticus 23:42*

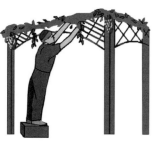

The joyous festival of Sukkot (Feast of Booths) begins five days after Yom Kippur on the fifteenth day of

Tishrei and is a sharp contrast to the somber tone of Yom Kippur. Sukkot is both a historical and an agricultural holiday, and is referred to as *Z'man Simchateinu*, the Season of our Rejoicing.

*"I caused the children of Israel to dwell in Sukkot, when I brought them out of the land of Egypt."*

Historically, Sukkot commemorates the exodus of the Jews from Egypt and the forty years wandering in the desert which led up to receiving the Torah at Mount Sinai. Whereas agriculturally, Sukkot is a celebration marking the end of the harvest season.

Shmini Atzeret and Simchat Torah are celebrated right after Sukkot. During the festival of Sukkot, we are to "dwell" in the *sukkah*. This means sharing a meal in the *sukkah*. It is a great time to invite family and friends to join you for a meal in the *sukkah*.

A *sukkah* is a temporary structure, a hut, made of three or four walls with covering that is made of something that is naturally grown, such as palm fronds. The *sukkah* should be deemed fit enough in which to live. To make sure it is built as a temporary structure, you should be able to see the stars in the sky through the roof covering when sitting in the *sukkah*.

Sukkot is an exciting, joyful holiday and one that encourages the participation of the whole family. Children will have fun building and decorating the *sukkah*, and they can help with the preparation of the food.

# SIMCHAT TORAH
# THE CELEBRATION OF THE TORAH

Immediately following the seven day festival of Sukkot comes the joyous holiday of Simhat Torah—the celebration of the Torah. The reading of the Torah starts at the beginning with the Book of Genesis. It is basically the new year of the Torah, which is the core document of the Jewish people. Typically, Jews come to the synagogue to sing songs and dance with the Torah.

We sing praises to G-d and the Torah. Traditionally, children march with apples and flags and sing and dance. This is called the "*Hakafot*" (procession). It is a wonderful day of celebrating and rejoicing with the Torah.

# WINTER HOLIDAY
# CHANUKAH

### The Festival of Lights

All over the world, an excitement fills the air of our Jewish homes as Chanukah approaches. The winter holiday of Chanukah (meaning "dedication") is the "Festival of Lights." It is a historical eight-day festival of dedication, which begins on the twenty-fifth day of the month of Kislev. Chanukah commemorates the rededication of the temple in Jerusalem. It is a holiday of freedom that celebrates the liberation of Israel by the Maccabees, a small band of Jewish soldiers. Chanukah commemorates the dedication miracle where a small amount of purified oil, only enough oil for one day, was lit to rededicate the Temple in Jerusalem and miraculously lasted for eight days. We enjoy traditional foods such as *latkes* or donuts. *Latkes* are potato pancakes fried in oil and eaten with applesauce, or sour cream and jam. In Israel, Israelis enjoy "*Sufganiot*" (jelly donuts), which are symbolic holiday treats.

On Chanukah, children and adults alike light the Chanukiah or Menorah (a candlelabra), sing songs, eat *latkes* and play the *dreidel* game. On the sides of the *dreidel* are the Hebrew letters *nun, gimmel, hay, shin*, the initial letters in the Hebrew saying "*Nes gadol hayah sham*," meaning "*A great miracle happened there*" commemorating the miracle of the Chanukah oil. We light the candles, one for each night, with the *Shamash*, the helper candle, until all eight candles are aglow. Chanukah is a joyous family time filled with warmth and tradition, and is often a child's favorite holiday.

# TU B'SHVAT – NEW YEAR OF THE TREES

*"Every blade of grass has its angel*
*that bends over it and whispers,*
*'Grow, grow'."*
—TALMUD

Tu B'Shvat is the tree holiday which is observed on the fifteenth (*tu*- the number 15 in Hebrew) of Shvat in the Jewish calendar, which is in late January or early February. The New Year of the Trees is also known as Jewish Arbor Day. Tu B'Shvat is the New Year for the purpose of calculating the age of the trees for tithing. Leviticus 19:23-25 states that fruit from trees may not be eaten during the first three years; the fourth year's fruit is for G-d. After that we can eat the fruit. Tu B'Shvat is an agricultural festival marking the emergence of Spring. Today, Tu B'Shvat has become the tree planting festival in Israel in which Jews all over the world plant trees in honor or in memory of a loved one or friend. You can also plant trees in Israel year round, and it's a very special support of Eretz Yisroel, Hebrew for The Land of Israel, to do this Mitzvah. For more information about planting trees (and forests!) in Israel, please contact: *www.jnftrees.org*. It is customary during this holiday to eat a new fruit and to partake in fruits that come from the Land of Israel.

Even though Tu B'Shvat is not considered to be one of the major holidays, it is a special one for me. Planting a tree reminds me of raising children. Here we plant a young tree, we nurture it to grow to be strong and healthy, just like our children.

# EARLY SPRING HOLIDAY
# PURIM

Here is another story of the survival of the Jewish people. The Jews who lived in Persia were about to be exterminated in a devious scheme of

Haman, the king's advisor. Queen Esther, the king's favorite, risked her life and rushed to inform the king of the plot against her people. The king reversed the outcome by saving the Jews and hanging Haman.

Purim is one of the most fun and joyous holidays for the children. It is customary to dress up in costumes and make a lot of noise. Which kid would not like that? During the reading of the *Megilah* (the story of Purim), we boo and make loud noises using noisemakers, every time we hear the name Haman.

Purim is a day of feasting and drinking. It is a Mitzvah to send *mishloach manot* (sending gifts of food) to friends and family, or giving Tzedakkah.

The traditional food on Purim is called Hamentachen. It is a triangle shaped pastry that resembles Haman's hat. In Hebrew it is called *ozen haman* (Haman's ear). I included a recipe for Hamentachen in the recipe section. So, eat drink and be merry.

# PASSOVER (PESACH)

### The Holiday of Freedom
The Jewish spring festival of Pesach, the holiday of Passover, begins on the fifteenth day of Nissan and lasts for seven days. Passover celebrates the exodus of the Jewish people out of Egypt, from slavery to freedom.

Passover has always been my favorite Jewish holiday, from when I was a child. I loved the Passover Model Seder that we had at Sunday School. We would put a hard boiled egg on a fork in one hand and a boiled potato on a fork in the other hand and say the blessing. Some families have other customs, such as holding a hard boiled egg and Matzah on top of your head, while reciting the *Ma Nishtanah* song. My favorite memories of Passover revolve around the wonderful foods and aromas!

My husband remembers Passover as the most significant celebration in his childhood, too. His family used to sing and dance all night long, and didn't stop until they could see the sun rise.

The holiday of Passover requires a lot of preparation and spring cleaning. Ashkenazi and Sepharadic customs may vary. Synagogues often hold classes for preparing and conducting the Seder.

Passover is a great celebration and a golden opportunity to bring the family together. Each aspect of the Passover celebration—the *Haggadah*, the Seder Plate, the meal, the *Afikomen* and more—gives you unique opportunities to be creative in your own family traditions. Make it a holiday you look forward to as a family. Invite friends and family to join you and share the joy. If family members are already hosting the first night's Seder, you can host the second night.

If you are unable to prepare for the Seder at you home, do not despair. Many synagogues sponsor Pesach Seders all around the country, and I am sure you can attend one in your area.

There are many customs that signify the importance of freedom from slavery. Reclining on pillows or cushions, or having someone else fill your glass of wine are such examples.

It is interesting, though, that Judaism, being a humanitarian religion, even though commanding us to celebrate our victory and freedom, does not want us to rejoice at the suffering of our enemy. That is why we take some wine out of our cup of wine, out of our joy and happiness, when we mention the plagues that G-d had inflicted on the Egyptians.

Just like we break the glass during the wedding ceremony, to remember the destruction of the temple, we have some rituals during Passover to recall the dark days of slavery. We dip a potato in salt water, which symbolizes the tears of our ancestors, and we eat *charoset*, which resembles the mortar that the Jews were using in their hard labor as slaves. During the Seder, we are asked to eat bitter herbs, which none of the kids like to comply with, in order to commemorate the bitter life we had in Egypt.

### "Next year in Jerusalem" The Haggadah

The Passover story is written in the *Haggadah*, which is the Hebrew word meaning "narration," "telling," or "recital." The Passover *Haggadah* is our written guidebook to the Passover experience and the Passover Seder, the ritual celebration and meal. The word Seder means order as in having order. The reading of the *Haggadah* and the Passover rituals at the Seder follow the same order each year as we follow and participate in the story of the Israelites making their way out of Egypt and out of slavery.

The Seder is not just a feast. The most profound purpose of the Seder, in my opinion, is the duty to tell the story of our survival to our children.

> *"He who does not increase knowledge, decreases it."*
> —RABBI HILLEL

In every generation, there is someone who rises up to destroy the Jewish nation, and we need to make our children and grandchildren aware of the dangers by telling this story. It has been said that history is bound to repeat itself unless we take steps to prevent it.

It is important to note that the story of Passover is written in the first person. We tell the story as if "we were slaves in Egypt." We feel our people's bitterness by eating the bitter herbs and we rejoice our nation's freedom by drinking wine. There is a strong connection throughout the generations.

The *Haggadah* is your guidebook for the Seder and the telling of the Passover exodus. It is filled with symbolism, songs, commentary and discussion. You will find *Haggadot* with a variety of customs from one community to another.

Have fun exploring the options available as you decide on the type of *Haggadah* that best fits you and your family's seder.

### Matzah

Prior to the first night of Passover, we prepare the home for Pesach  by clearing all *chametz*. *Chametz* is defined as any leavened bread products, as well as any product containing wheat, barley, oats, spelt or rye that may have risen. In addition, Ashkenazi tradition forbids eating rice, beans, corn and other legumes. Sephardic tradition does allow rice, beans,

L'Mazeltov

corn and other legumes during Pesach. Removing the *chametz* from the home can be a fun activity for children.

During Passover, we refrain from eating leavened bread and instead we eat *matzah*. Strict rabbinical rules govern the production of *matzah* that is *Kosher* for Passover.

*Matzah* is a very significant symbol of the exodus from Egypt and the Passover story. *Matzah* is the true "soul food" —the stripped down bread which is *matzah* with no additives or even yeast, just the essence is there. When the Israelites fled Egypt, they did not have time to allow their bread to rise and had to bake it quickly. Today we share this experience by eating unleavened bread.

## The Seder Plate

The Seder plate is a special decorative plate used specifically for Passover. It is designed to hold five or six items, depending on customs, that symbolize a variety of aspects of the holiday. During this celebration of freedom we explain the use of these symbols and their significance to our heritage. The symbolic items are:

**Maror** – Bitter herbs (grated horseradish) that represent the bitterness and hardship we had endured as slaves.

**Charoset** – A sweet, brown chunky mixture made of walnuts, honey, apples, wine, and cinnamon and dates symbolizes the mortar used by the Jewish slaves for building with bricks (see recipe section).

**Karpas** – A vegetable, usually parsley, celery or a boiled potato, dipped in salt water, which represents the tears shed by the Jewish slaves. A vegetable also signifies a simple food, the only food the slaves could eat.

**Z'roa** – A roasted lamb shank bone representing the Pesach sacrifice. In vegetarian homes, the lamb shank is often substituted with a large roasted beet. It also reminds us of the sacrifice used to mark the door posts of the Jewish homes in Egypt, so that the angel of death would "pass over" them, when he inflicted harm on the Egyptians.

**Beitzah** – A roasted or hard boiled egg. For some, it is a symbol of mourning over the destruction of the temple. Others say it is symbolic of the cycle of life.

## Ma Nishtana — The Four Questions

"Ma Nishtana" literally translates as "What is different" and refers to the four questions asked during the Passover Seder. Everyone at the Seder, especially the children, share the honor of asking the four questions. "Ma Nishtana" is usually sung to a traditional melody. The main question is, "Why is this night different from all other nights?" "*Ma nishtana halayla hazeh meekol haleylot?*" These are the four questions:

1. *Why do we eat bread and matzah on all other nights of the year, but on this night we can only eat matzah?*
2. *Why do we eat all kinds of herbs on all other nights, but on this night we eat bitter herbs?*
3. *Why don't we dip our herbs even once on all other nights, but on this night we dip them twice?*
4. *Why is it that we sit straight or in a reclining position on all other nights, but on this particular night we eat in the reclining position?*

The *Hagaddah* includes the answers that will be read after the questions are recited. Generally at Passover, each participant at the Seder will take a turn telling the Passover story, as they read from the *Haggadah*. This celebration of freedom and everything shared at the Seder is designed to heighten a child's curiosity and invite them to ask questions.

## The Afikomen

The *Afikomen* is a piece of Matzah that is hidden at the beginning of the Seder. The Seder cannot be concluded until the *Afikomen*, the dessert, is eaten. The children are encouraged, to find the *Afikomen* and get a reward for it. This is one of the games, designed to entertain the children and to keep their interest until the end of the Seder. For most children, this is the highlight of the Seder. Traditions for searching for the *Afikomen* vary. Traditionally, the youngest children search the house for the *Afikomen*. Once they find it, they will "sell" it back to the head of the family for the "right" price. Other family members can help the child with their negotiation skills. There are some other variations

L'Mazeltov

to this game. Whatever tradition your family embraces, you can make this an enjoyable experience for all.

### Elijah the Prophet

At a *Brit Milah*, at the Passover Seder and at the close of *Shabbat*, we honor and make reference to Elijah the Prophet. At the Passover Seder, we open the door and set aside a cup of wine for Elijah the Prophet. Elijah is seen as our guardian angel, our protector, and his presence will signal the arrival of the Messiah.

# SHAVUOT – FESTIVAL OF WEEKS

Fifty days after Passover, we celebrate Shavuot—the Festival of Weeks. Although it is least observed by non religious Jews, it has very significant meaning. Shavuot commemorates the anniversary of the day the Torah was given to the Jews at Mount Sinai. Shavuot is one of the three Jewish pilgrim festivals that involve all night studying. The other two holidays are Passover and Sukkot. It is customary to eat dairy dishes such as blintzes and kugels (see recipe section), as a symbol of the Torah that is sweet like milk and honey. Also, it honors the laws of keeping Kosher, as there were no separate dishes for dairy and meat while the children of Israel lived in the desert. Shavuot also commemorates the "counting of the Omer"—which is counting a full seven weeks (fifty days) from Passover to Shavuot and the offering of new grain to G-d.

> *"My judgement will be a light for all people to whom I will give rest."*
> —Isaiah 51:4

Judaism cherishes each child and encourages their participation in holiday celebrations. These festivities are a positive and powerful way to connect children to family and Judaism.

# JEWISH LIFE CYCLE IN SUMMARY

*"seedlings turn overnight to sunflowers,
blossoming even as we gaze ..."*

During my research for L'Mazeltov, I discovered that our Jewish population is shrinking while the world's population is increasing in number. I believe there are many reasons for this alarming situation. Some were caused by the Holocaust, wars in Israel or terrorist attacks. Anti-Semitism worldwide still causes our Jewish People to go underground and blend into the mainstream population. I believe the main reason that our Jewish population is dwindling is due to assimilation. Many Jews intermarry which can lead to assimilation and a decrease in our numbers.

We, the Jewish People, have such a rich and beautiful tradition and history, that it is so sad to have it fade away. This is why I decided to embark on this long journey, hoping to promote the values and traditions of our wonderful heritage.

I hope that L'Mazeltov can be a spark to help you plant strong roots of Judaism in your home starting now, while you are expecting your precious new baby. By raising a Jewish child, you are contributing a meaningful link that connects all of us from one generation to another —L'Dor V'Dor.

# SECTION IV

# Traditional
# L'Mazeltov
# Recipes

"He who has fed a stranger
may have fed an angel."
—TALMUD

# Recipes

## BUBBE'S CHICKEN SOUP

### Great for Shabbat and Holiday Meals

1    4-5 lb. chicken cut-up into large pieces.
3-4 quarts of cold water
Salt and pepper to taste
1-2 whole onions, chopped
4    large carrots, cut diagonally
4    celery stalks, cut in pieces
2    medium bay leaves, 2 bunches of fresh parsley, chopped
1    cube of chicken bouillon
Optional: peeled potatoes cut into cubes

1.  Clean and wash the chicken pieces in cold water. Place into a large soup pot and add enough water to cover the chicken. Cover and bring to boil. Skim the foam. Add salt and pepper to taste. Add veggies, fresh herbs, and bouillon. Cover and simmer on low heat for 2-3 hours until chicken falls off the bone.

*Your home will smell delicious! Enjoy!*

# HAPPY CHALLAH DAYS

## For Shabbat and Holidays

1     package yeast
2     teaspoons sugar
1½ cup warm water
4½ cups flour
2     teaspoons salt
2     eggs
2     tablespoons oil

1. Combine the yeast, sugar, and ½ lukewarm cup warm water. Let stand 5 minutes. Add the flour and salt into the bowl. In the center of the bowl, add the eggs and oil, 1 cup of water and the yeast mixture. Knead into the flour.
2. Place the dough into an oiled bowl, and brush with a little oil. Cover with a towel and let the dough rise (Place in a warm area). Let it rise until it has doubled in size.
3. Divide the dough into three parts. Shape each section into a 15 inch rope. Braid the ropes and pinch the ends to seal. Place on the baking pan.
4. Cover and let rise again in a warm area. Brush with egg yolk and sprinkle with optional poppy or sesame seeds. Bake at 375 degrees for 30 minutes until golden brown. Makes one large Challah.

*What a special treat on your* Shabbat *table!*

# TRADITIONAL CHOLENT (MEAT)

## A Delicious and Easy Shabbat Stew

½  pound dried beans (lima, navy, chickpeas, pinto or a mix)
3  pounds potatoes, cubed
1½ pound lean meat, cubed
3  large onions, cubed
2  tablespoon flour
1  teaspoon salt
Pepper to taste
2-3 cloves garlic, crushed
¼  teaspoon paprika
4  quarts water

1. Soak beans in water overnight. Drain. Place all ingredients in a 8 quart pot and cover up to the top with water. Bring to a boil.
   *(A large Dutch oven or large crockpot is perfect for cholent.)*
2. Lower heat and cover tightly. Cook overnight at 250 degrees for 24 hours or 350 degrees for 4 - 5 hours.

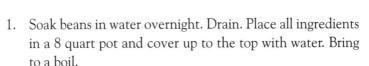

**TIPS:** Make sure that there is enough water so the cholent does not get dry. Check the water level a few times during these hours.

*Your home will be filled with an amazing aroma! It's a good idea to eat a small quantity of cholent for Shabbat lunch, as it is a heavy meal that makes you want to take a Shabbat nap!*

# MAMA'S MANDELBROT

## Almond Cookies

### THE ULTIMATE DIPPING COOKIE

3    eggs
1    cup oil
1    cup sugar
1    teaspoon almond extract
3½ cups flour
2    teaspoon baking powder
½    cup chopped almonds

1. Beat eggs, add oil, sugar and almond extract and continue to beat.
2. Combine the flour and baking powder together and then add to egg mixture. You can use a wooden spoon or your hands for a smoother texture. Add the almonds and form into 4 loaves.
3. Bake on a greased cookie sheet at 350 degrees for 30 minutes. Slice right away into dipping cookies and then bake for 5 more minutes.

*Very yummy! Brew some coffee or tea and enjoy!*

# HONEY CAKE (ROSH HASHANA)

5 cups flour
1 teaspoon baking soda
1 tablespoon baking powder
½ teaspoon salt
½ teaspoon cinnamon
½ teaspoon ginger
½ teaspoon cloves
½ teaspoon nutmeg
4 eggs
1 cup vegetable oil
1 cup lemon juice
1 cup orange juice

*Bring the following ingredients to a boil and cool:*

1 cup black coffee or strong tea
1 cup honey
1 cup brown sugar
1 cup granulated sugar
Slivered almonds (optional)

1. Beat eggs, add vegetable oil and fruit juices. Add the pre-mixed dry ingredients, alternating with the honey mixture that was boiled and cooled.
2. Sprinkle the slivered almonds on top if you like. Bake in a 9 x 12 inch loaf pain at 350 degrees for approximately 1 and ¼ hours.
3. Cool and slice.

*Bring in the New Year with this traditional, sweet dessert!*

# LITAL'S LATKES

## For Chanukah

5   large potatoes
1   large onion
4   eggs
1   teaspoon salt
Pinch of pepper
2   tablespoons matzah meal
Vegetable oil for frying

1. Peel potatoes and onion.
2. Grate potatoes and onion.
3. Mix together the eggs, salt, pepper, matzah meal, grated potatoes and onion.
4. Use a wooden spoon to mix together all the ingredients.
5. Pour oil into a large frying pan—get the oil hot.
6. By the spoonful, place the mixture into the pan (carefully, due to hot oil!).
7. Fry the latkes about 4 minutes on each side until crispy and brown.

*Serve with applesauce, sour cream or strawberry jam—So tasty!*

# SAUTA MIRIAM'S SUFGANIOT

## Chanukah Donuts

3   cups flour
2   tablespoon oil
¼   teaspoon salt
2   large egg yolks
2   packages active dry yeast
¾   cup lukewarm water
4   tablespoon sugar
(Powdered sugar to coat and jelly for filling)

1. Put the yeast in a small cup and add a little water and sugar. Let it rise few minutes.
2. Add the yeast to the rest of the ingredients (except powdered sugar and jelly) and knead well. Let the dough rise. Form dough into balls and let it rise again.
3. Fry in deep oil. When bottom gets golden brown, turn donuts over to brown the other side.
4. Take out of oil and drain. Inject jelly with an injector and then spread some powdered sugar on top.
5. Serve hot.

*There is nothing like homemade donuts!*

# ESTHER'S HAMENTACHEN

## A Purim Delight

1   cup shortening
3   cups flour
1   teaspoon baking powder
½   cup orange juice
½   teaspoon salt

Fillings: apricot preserves, prune preserves,
     or poppy seed filling. Use any jams or check out the Kosher
     aisle in your market for fillings.
1   cup sugar
2   eggs, beaten

1. Mix dry ingredients (except the sugar) together in a small
   bowl. Using a wooden spoon, beat the oil, eggs, and orange
   juice, then add the sugar and beat all together in a large
   bowl. Add the flour mixture one cup at a time and combine
   well. Wrap in plastic wrap and refrigerate overnight.
2. Roll out dough on a wooden board dusted with flour. Use a
   coffee mug as a cookie cutter to form approximately three-
   inch rounds.
3. Place a teaspoon of filling in the center of each round. Fold
   three spots in toward the center to form a triangle. Pinch
   the sides together with moistened fingertips.
4. Bake on a greased cookie sheet at 350 degrees for about
   20-25 minutes until golden brown.

*Eat with a cold glass of milk. Enjoy!*

# THE SEDER PLATE

## Special for Passover

**Karpas** - Parsley, potatoes, onions or vegetables
**Maror** - bitter herbs, like horseradish
**Beitzah** - hard boiled egg
**Charoseth** - apples and nuts, wine and cinnamon (you can add pears or dates)
**Pesach** - Shank bone of lamb
**Salt water**

### CHAROSET FOR PASSOVER
*Apple and nut mixture representing the mortar between the bricks.*

2  apples
½  cups chopped walnuts
1  tablespoon honey
2  tablespoon Kosher wine
½ to 1 teaspoon cinnamon
White or yellow raisins

1. Peel the apples and core. Chop into small pieces. You may add chopped dates or pears, also. Pour into a bowl.
2. Add the chopped nuts, honey, wine, cinnamon, and the raisins, combine all together.

*Delicious on a piece of matzah!*

# MATZAH BALLS FOR PASSOVER

4    eggs
½   cup cold club soda (makes the matzah balls light!)
1    teaspoon salt
½   cup vegetable oil
1    cup matzah meal
3    tablespoons ice cold water

1. Beat the eggs, add the club soda, and cold water.
2. Add the salt, vegetable oil, and stir in the matzah meal. Refrigerate several hours or overnight.
3. With wet hands from cold water, form the matzah balls and add them one at a time to a big pot of boiling water. Cook for approximately 20-30 minutes. Drain and drop them into your already prepared hot chicken soup.

*Everyone will praise your delicious matzah ball soup!*

# PAMELA'S FAMOUS KUGEL

*PREHEAT OVEN TO 400 DEGREES.*

1     stick of butter, melt in large bowl in microwave 1 minute
2/3    cup canola oil
½     teaspoon salt
1     teaspoon vanilla
4     beaten eggs
16 oz. cottage cheese
16 oz. sour cream
1     cup white sugar
½     cup brown sugar
12 oz. wide egg noodles (uncooked)
8     cups milk
½     cup golden raisins
Cinnamon to sprinkle on top
*Use wooden spoon*

1. Mix all ingredients, except last 4 ingredients, on the list.
2. Add noodles, then add milk and raisins. Pour into 2 rectangular glass pans. Sprinkle with cinnamon and put in preheated oven set at 400 degrees.
3. Start baking at 400 degrees for about 15 minutes, and reduce to 375 degrees.
4. Bake for a total of approximately 1 hour and 20 minutes. Check if done and continue to bake until golden brown and not bubbling. Cool to room temperature and then refrigerate. *It is much easier to cut into small squares when it is cold. You can warm it up in the microwave before serving.*

*B'Tayavon—Hebrew for good appetite!*

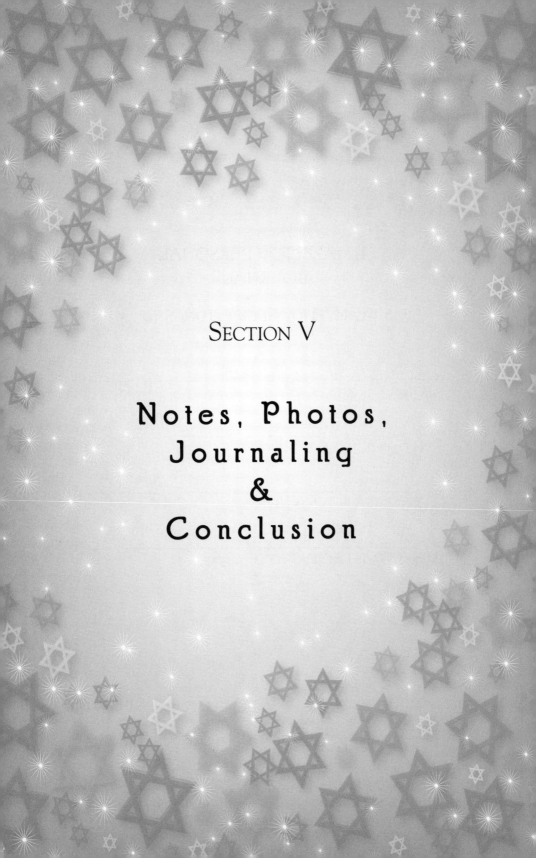

SECTION V

Notes, Photos,
Journaling
&
Conclusion

# L'MAZELTOV PERSONAL JOURNAL

## MY L'MAZELTOV BOOK BELONGS TO:

_____

NAME

_____

DATE

_____

CITY, STATE, OR COUNTRY

_____

THIS BOOK IS DEDICATED TO

# L'Mazeltov Workbook

*"Just as my ancestors planted for me, so shall I plant for my children."*

—*Tanit 32a*

Since our main goal is to preserve and celebrate our traditions as a Jewish People with an emphasis on faith, culture, and importance of family, we provide this section for you to make this book your own. Journal writing can be a voyage to chart the milestones and blessings in one's life.

- In this workbook write down your joys and events during the miraculous time of pregnancy and birth.
- Let your heart touch all the blessings that have been brought into your life by including photos and mementos that will bring back delightful memories.
- Let this book become a treasure to hand down to the grown child for whom the recollections are dedicated.
- It will be a gift when they too become a parent and begin life's journey anew.

My *first impressions*— *how I felt when I first learned the news that I am going to have a baby!*

_____

_____

_____

_____

_____

*How I feel during the first trimester of pregnancy (1–3 months)*

_____

_____

_____

_____

_____

*How I feel during the second trimester of pregnancy (4 – 6 months)*

_____

_____

_____

_____

_____

L'Mazeltov

*How I feel during the third and last trimester of pregnancy*
*(7 – 9 months)*

_____

_____

_____

_____

_____

*Hopes and dreams I have for my child*
*(for the expectant mother)*

_____

_____

_____

_____

*Hopes and dreams I have for my child*
*(for the expectant father)*

_____

_____

_____

_____

# BABY'S NAMING CEREMONY

*Journaling and Photos*

# BABY'S FIRST HOLIDAYS

*Journaling, Photos & Notes*

# BABY'S FIRST SHABBAT, CHANUKAH, PASSOVER, ROSH HASHANA

*Journaling and Photos*

# Conclusion

*"To have roots is the most important need that we have and the least recognized need of the human soul."*

## ENJOY THE JOURNEY

I am so glad that you have had the opportunity to read L'Mazeltov, a blending of Childbirth with Jewish Life Cycle education. It is good to know that you are a part of the celebration and you have a community that supports you and rejoices in your journey of building the foundation of your Jewish home.

We hope that L'Mazeltov will encourage you to plant stronger Jewish roots as you prepare for the spiritual, emotional and physical birth of your precious new baby. May you have the wings to flourish as loving parents in your own families.

We are blessed that you have made L'Mazeltov a part of your experience. We toast you with Mazel Tov and L'Chaim on the birth of your new baby and this new phase of life as Jewish parents.

*"May G-d bless you and keep you, May he let his countenance shine upon you and be gracious unto you all the days of your lives."* Amen.

THE L'MAZELTOV COMMUNITY WEBSITE
**www.lmazeltov.org**

# About the Author

*"The Mitzvah of L'Mazeltov is Pamela's 'dream come true' for Jewish expectant parents and their families."*

Pamela S. Nadav is a practicing Women's Health Nurse Practitioner, Obstetrical Registered Nurse, UCLA Certified Childbirth Educator, Women's Health Lecturer, Hebrew and religious school teacher, and the author of L'Mazeltov as well as other educational topics, including Menopause.

She has over 30 years of experience in Maternal Child Health nursing and over 12 years of experience as a Women's Health Nurse Practitioner. She has worked for several years specifically in labor and delivery and has taught for many years as a Childbirth Educator at local colleges, clinics, hospitals, and synagogues.

A graduate of the Harbor-UCLA Women's Health Nurse Practitioner Program, and the USC School of Nursing, Pamela graduated with honors. She earned her Childbirth Educator Certification at UCLA. Active in Jewish youth organizations throughout her youth, Pamela attended Jewish summer camps in California, including Camp Ramah and Camp Alonim at the Brandeis-Bardin Institute. Pamela went to Israel at age 18 years old to study Hebrew, Judaic studies, and theater arts at the Tel Aviv University. She also lived on a kibbutz in Israel for one year as a Kibbutz Nurse. Years later, Pamela returned to

Camp Alonim as Camp Nurse for several summers with her children as campers.

Pamela lives in Carlsbad, California with her husband, Yoav, and they enjoy grown children and a new generation of precious grandchildren. They love being "Saba and Savta" and bringing Jewish values into the lives of their family. The Mitzvah of L'Mazeltov is Pamela's "dream come true" for Jewish expectant parents and their families.

# About the L'Mazeltov Affiliate Program

*"Jewish expectant parents: our most valuable role models for the next generation."*

## THE L'MAZELTOV COMMUNITY

For Synagogues and Jewish Community Centers who wish to host a L'Mazeltov Program, this is for you.

As a L'Mazeltov affiliate you will be joining a distinguished community of educators dedicated to enriching the lives of new Jewish parents by providing community, education and resources. Our goal is to provide support and education to new Jewish parents during their pregnancy and to help them build a Jewish home environment and community in which to raise their children. L'Mazeltov is designed to benefit all those involved—educators, synagogues, community centers, organizations and participants. From its inception 20 years ago, L'Mazeltov has been committed to the Jewish community, Tikkun Olam and L' Dor V'Dor. We wholeheartedly welcome you to L'Mazeltov and look forward to connecting with you soon.

*We invite you to contact us at:*
**L'Mazeltov**
P.O. Box 729, Carlsbad, CA 92018
Tel: 800 604-9844 • **www.lmazeltov.org** • baby@lmazeltov.org

# Notes

# Endorsements

"This book is the product of a very good mind and a very good heart. Read it. You'll love it, and it will change your life 'for good'!"

—RABBI MARVIN BORNSTEIN, LOS ANGELES, CA

಄

"This is a delightfully perceptive book! Every new Jewish parent should be given a copy of *L'Mazeltov*. It is just the sort of guidebook that has the potential to be a parenting classic for those who want to integrate sound obstetrical information with essential Jewish values and customs."

—SAN DIEGO JEWISH JOURNAL

಄

"L'Mazeltov is a one-of-a-kind book for Jewish families! It is a great reference resource for every Jewish expectant mother to have as she goes through the miracle of childbirth. It is full of tradition, facts, and pregnancy advice that is easy to read for the entire family!"

—DR. EINAT DUHAMEL, MD (OBSTETRICS & GYNECOLOGY)

಄

"L'Mazeltov is a fascinating journey. It should be included in every expectant Jewish couple's library, so that they can leave their children great memories and a tradition to follow."

—DR. MOSHE AND DIANA ZWANG, authors of *Palm Therapy*

"Over and over again I hear Pam's calm and balanced Jewish approach to life as the foundation for her inspiring book. I guess you could say she's the ultimate Jewish mother!"

—DR. DEBORAH ECKSTEIN KATZ, Psychologist

❧

"I was so happy to discover the L'Mazeltov program at my local synagogue. I wanted to be able to form relationships with other mothers to meet for playgroups and Jewish holidays and L'Mazeltov was the perfect place to find them!"

—GWEN DAMSKY-COHEN, RN (L'MAZELTOV ALUMNUS)

❧

"L'Mazeltov holds out a wonderful ideal for women and their families. It is my hope that this book helps keep kids Jewish by giving them a glimpse of the culture and tradition that so many of us have been privileged to experience and love."

—SHERRY BROWN, SCHOOL TEACHER